HIGH SCHOOL HEALTH 5

D1489572

CONTENTS

Author: Krista White, B.S.
Editor: Al Christopherson, M.S.
Illustrations: Laura Miller/Alpha Omega Staff

Alpha Omega Publications®

804 N. 2nd Ave. E., Rock Rapids, IA 51246-1759
© MMI by Alpha Omega Publications, Inc.   All rights reserved.
LIFEPAC is a registered trademark of Alpha Omega Publications, Inc.

LIFEPAC®

High School Health
Student Book

Unit 5

Alpha Omega Publications®

OVERVIEW

The Garden of Eden was the picture of perfect health. There was no pain, death, or suffering of any kind. That changed, however, when Adam disobeyed God. As our divinely appointed representative, Adam's fall brought the curse of death upon mankind. In I Corinthians 15:22, Paul states, "in Adam all die." Sickness and disease are a direct result of the fall. They are reminders of God's condemning pronouncement, "for dust thou art, and unto dust shalt thou return" (Genesis 3:19).

Adam's sin corrupted not only mankind, it also corrupted the earth. "Cursed is the ground for your sake," God announced, indicating the "futility" that all physical matter would be subjected to until the whole creation was delivered from a state of imperfection and decay.

In this LIFEPAC® you will discover the relationship between the health of your body and your environment. You will study common diseases, attaining a general knowledge of their causes and their prevention. You will also study various types of drugs, gaining an understanding of their functions and factors that lead to their abuse. Finally, you will learn about the state of the environment, and its importance to your health.

OBJECTIVES

When you have completed this LIFEPAC, you should be able to:

*   Understand the origin of disease.

*   Understand the role and the power of medicine in the fight against disease.

*   Differentiate between drug use and drug abuse.

*   Explain the biblical view of alcohol and tobacco use.

*   Discern the role mankind has to play in regards to preserving the environment.

*   Understand the relationship between the state of the environment and your health.

VOCABULARY

Acute – brief and intense

Antediluvian – of the period before the Flood

Biodegradable – susceptible to decomposition by living organisms

Chronic – continuing for a long time

Congenital – existing from birth

Corrosive – capable of destroying by a chemical action

Euphoria – feeling of well-being not necessarily based in reality

Malady – disease

Non-infectious – non-communicable; cannot be spread through casual contact
          or any mechanism of transmission such as air, water, or blood

Organic – derived from plants or animals

Particulate – tiny particle that can be dispersed in a gas

Pathogen – disease-causing agent

Phagocytes – white blood cells that eliminate the chances of infection by attacking foreign substances in the body

Putrefaction – the decay of organic matter caused by microorganisms

Refuse – waste

Subservient – in a subordinate position

Vector – an animal or insect that is known to transmit a specific disease

Viable – capable of life

I. DISEASE AND PREVENTION

In the Garden of Eden, Adam and Eve enjoyed perfect health under God's provisions in the covenant of works, the moral agreement established by God in which total obedience would result in life and disobedience would result in death. Adam and Eve lived in joyous harmony with God, each other, and the rest of Creation.

When Adam and Eve ate of the tree of the knowledge of good and evil, they violated the covenant of works, bringing the curse of death upon themselves. Before God drove Adam and Eve out of the Garden of Eden, He pronounced, "In the sweat of thy face shalt thou eat bread, till thou return unto the ground; for out of it wast thou taken; for dust thou art, and unto dust shalt thou return" (Genesis 3:19).

As our divinely appointed representative, Adam's fall was our fall. "Therefore, as by the offence of one judgment came upon all men to condemnation...For as by one man's disobedience many were made sinners..." (Romans 5:18a, 19a). Adam's disobedience made us all sinners. Conceived and born in sin (Psalm 51:5), we are all under the curse of death.

Because humans consist of both soul and body, the curse of death has both moral and physical ramifications. "Wherefore, as by one man sin entered into the world, and death by sin; and so death passed upon all men, for that all have sinned" (Romans 5:12). Paul describes the moral ramifications of the fall by stating that we are dead in our trespasses and sins—that we are prone to speak, do, and pursue all kinds of evil (Romans 3:10–18).

The physical ramifications of the fall are the pain of childbirth, the strain of work, and bodily deterioration. Disease and sickness are a direct result of the Fall. The physical pain and discomfort that illness inflicts are reminders that one day, "to dust [we] shall return."

However, as one commentator has noted, death is not only a judgment but a blessing. For the Christian, death brings about "eternal salvation that outlasts the grave." When Christ returns, He will remove the curse of sin from our bodies, transforming us into His likeness. Like the Garden of Eden, Heaven will be a place where disease and pain does not exist (Revelation 21:4). Believers will once again live in perfect communion with God, other people, and nature. In Heaven, we will enjoy the eternal blessings of Christ's total obedience.

Types of Infections

The dictionary defines disease as "the improper functioning of the body brought about by heredity, infection, diet, or the environment." Diseases that are caused by heredity, diet, or the environment are termed **non-infectious**. Non-infectious diseases are non-communicable; that is, they cannot be spread through casual contact or any mechanism of transmission such as air, water, or blood. An example of a non-infectious disease is cancer. Factors believed to contribute to the development of cancer include heredity, diet, and environment. You cannot get cancer by touching a person that is suffering from cancer.

Viral Infections. Infectious diseases are caused by the spread of harmful microorganisms, which can be categorized into six groups: viruses, bacteria, fungi, chlamydiae, rickettsiae, and protozoa. Viral infections are caused by the multiplication of a small infectious agent within the body known as a virus. Viruses cause disease by invading a host cell and then destroying it through replication. Depending upon the virus, an infection can be contracted through airborne transmission, waterborne transmission, blood-borne transmission, sexual transmission, or even direct contact. Examples of viral infections include chickenpox, influenza, AIDS, rabies, and viral meningitis.

Bacterial Infections. Similar to viral infections, bacterial infections are caused by the reproduction of a small infectious agent within the body. Bacterial infections can be contracted by breathing in infectious droplets, eating contaminated food, or exposing open wounds or mucus membranes to surfaces covered with pathogenic bacteria. Once in the body, pathogenic bacteria cause disease by producing poisons that destroy cells. Examples of bacterial infections include pneumonia, food poisoning, typhoid fever, and tonsillitis.

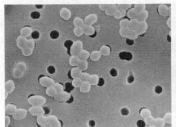 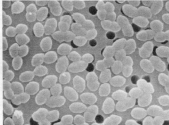 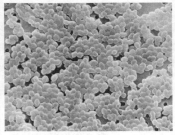 

Reproduction of Bacteria *Images courtesy of CDC*

Fungal Infections. Fungal infections are caused by the multiplication of fungal organisms on or in the body. Fungal infections usually occur when the body's immune system is impaired and is unable to keep the amount of fungi on or in the body at a healthy level. Fungi can cause disease by destroying or invading body tissues. Examples of fungal infections include athlete's foot, hay fever, mushroom poisoning, and candidiasis.

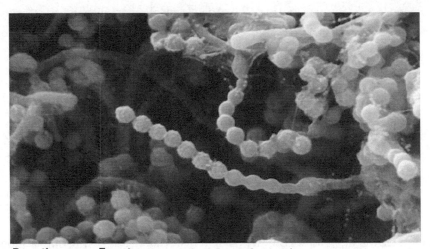

Paecilomyces Fungi (causes pulmonary infections) *Image courtesy of CDC*

Rickettsial Infections. Unlike chlamydial infections, which are caused by the invasion of a microorganism, rickettsial and protozoan infections are caused by microscopic parasites. Rickettsial and protozoan infections can be contracted through an insect bite or by eating contaminated food. Examples of rickettsial and protozoan infections include malaria and Rocky Mountain spotted fever.

The illustration on the following page shows the infection cycle of Rocky Mountain Spotted Fever.

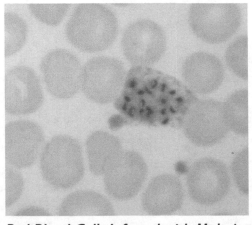 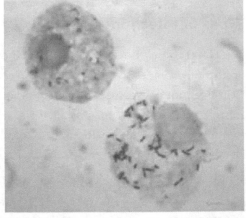

Red Blood Cells Infected with Malaria
Image courtesy of CDC

Cells infected with Rocky Mountain Spotted Fever *Image courtesy of CDC*

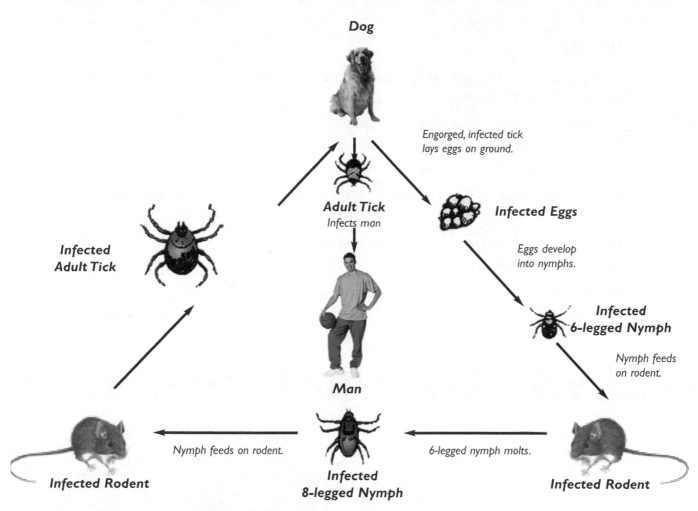

Infection Cycle for Rocky Mountain Spotted Fever

Short answer.

1.1   When was the only time mankind has ever experienced perfect health? _____

_____

_____

1.2   What are the four types of infections?

a. _____   b. _____

c. _____   d. _____

1.3   What are six categories of harmful microorganisms?

a. _____   b. _____

c. _____   d. _____

e. _____   f. _____

Matching.

1.4 _____ the improper functioning of the body brought about by heredity, infection, diet, or the environment

1.5 _____ cannot be spread through contact or any mechanism of transmission

1.6 _____ caused by the spread of harmful microorganisms

1.7 _____ caused by the multiplication of a small infectious agent which invades a host cell and then destroys it

1.8 _____ caused by the reproduction of a small infectious agent which produces poisons that destroy cells

1.9 _____ caused by the multiplication of fungal organisms on or in the body

1.10 _____ caused by microscopic parasites

a. bacterial infection

b. disease

c. fungal infection

d. infectious disease

e. non-infectious disease

f. protozoan infection

g. viral infection

The Immune System

The immune system protects the body from the threat of disease. Its effectiveness is directly related to your overall health. Eating right, getting enough rest, and managing stress properly will help your body fight against disease.

The immune system consists of two parts: innate immunity and adaptive immunity. Innate immunity is the system of defense that every human is born with. It consists of the skin, protective secretions, the inflammatory response, and **phagocytes**. If microorganisms are able to penetrate the physical barriers (the skin and protective secretions), the body responds in a nonspecific way by increasing the blood flow to the area. This allows phagocytes to take action. Phagocytes are white blood cells that eliminate the chances of infection by attacking foreign substances in the body.

If the innate immune system is unable to control the infection, the adaptive immune system responds by producing specific antibodies or the activation of killer cells to attack the invading microorganisms. The adaptive immune system consists of two parts: humoral immunity and cellular immunity. In humoral immunity, disease-specific antibodies are produced in order to attack and destroy harmful bacteria. For instance, if you contract pneumonia, your

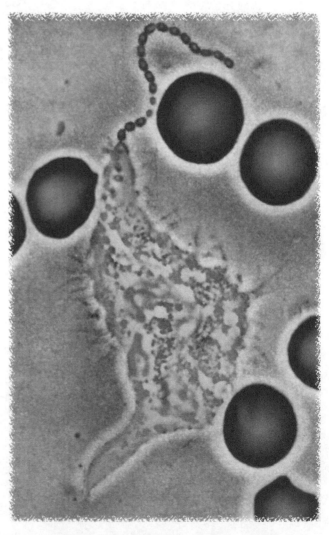

A White Blood Cell Attacking Bacteria

body will produce special cells that are specifically equipped to attack and destroy the pneumonia-causing bacteria (shown at right).

Once created, some antibodies stay in your body for the rest of your life. If you contract chicken pox when you are young, you probably will not suffer from the disease as an adult. Your immune system will keep antibodies specific to chicken pox circulating throughout your body.

Cellular immunity generally works to combat cancer cells, some viruses, and parasites. Defensive agents involved include helper cells and killer cells. Helper cells identify abnormal cells and alert killer cells to attack. Killer cells attach to abnormal cells, eventually destroying them.

Symptoms of Infection. Certain symptoms indicate that the body is trying to combat invading microorganisms. Inflammation or fever is usually the first sign that your immune system is at work. Inflammation occurs when the innate immune system is attempting to flush a specific area with phagocytes. A fever occurs when the adaptive immune system is combating invading microorganisms. It is the body's attempt to kill the disease-causing agents by increasing the temperature of their environment above that which is conducive to their existence.

Depending upon the disease or illness, symptoms beyond a fever or inflammation can vary. In order to get the needed treatment in a timely manner, it is important to watch the development of symptoms carefully. Many life-threatening illnesses initially manifest symptoms similar to the common cold.

Avoiding Infection. The easiest way to avoid the contraction of infectious diseases is to practice good hygiene. As pointed out in the section titled "Personal Hygiene" in Health LIFEPAC 3, cleanliness aids in the preservation of your health. Disease-causing organisms can be spread through casual contact, such as shaking hands or breathing in small particles of mucus expelled by a sneeze. Washing your hands, keeping your nails clean, and covering your mouth and nose when you cough and sneeze will help prevent the spread of pathogens.

The practice of good hygiene can also help avoid the spread of infectious diseases caused by eating food that is contaminated by disease-causing organisms. Food should be prepared and served with clean hands and utensils. Some foods such as chicken, beef, and eggs are particularly susceptible to contamination and should be cooked thoroughly before eating.

Avoiding close contact with animals or insects known to carry pathogens is yet another way to protect yourself from disease.

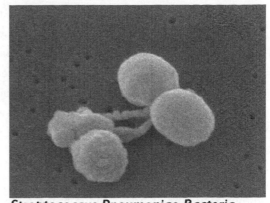

Streptococcus Pneumoniae Bacteria

Image courtesy of CDC

An animal or insect that is known to transmit a specific disease is termed a **vector**. For example, mosquitoes are vectors of the parasite that causes malaria. Avoiding regions that are infested by infected mosquitoes will help prevent you from contracting malaria. The deer tick is a vector of the organism that causes Lyme disease. If you live in a heavily-wooded area, check yourself and your pets frequently for these dangerous pests.

If you cannot avoid being exposed to certain disease-causing organisms, immunization can help prevent infection. Immunization helps boost the immune system by injecting weak or dead pathogens into the body. The body then builds up antibodies to fight against the disease. If infection occurs, the immune system will be well prepared to defeat the disease-causing agent. Over the last century, increased measures to immunize citizens of developed countries against infectious diseases such as polio, tetanus, measles, and the mumps have dramatically increased the average life expectancy.

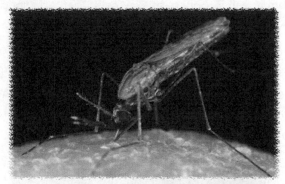

Anopheles Mosquito (Malaria)

Deer Tick (Lyme Disease)

Images courtesy of CDC

Fill in the blanks.

1.11 The body is protected from the threat of disease by the _____ system.

1.12 The _____ immune system consists of the skin, protective secretions, the inflammatory response, and phagocytes.

1.13 _____ are white blood cells that eliminate the chances of infection.

1.14 The _____ immune system is activated if the innate immune system is unable to control the infection.

1.15 _____ immunity depends upon the production of disease specific antibodies to destroy harmful bacteria.

1.16 _____ immunity uses helper cells and killer cells to identify and destroy abnormal cells.

1.17 _____ of infection indicate that the body is trying to combat invading microorganisms.

1.18 _____ occurs when the innate immune system is attempting to flush a specific area with phagocytes.

1.19 A _____ occurs when the adaptive immune system is combating invading microorganisms.

1.20 The contraction of infectious diseases can be avoided by practicing good _____ , avoiding contact with _____ , and boosting your immune system with _____ .

Recommended Childhood Immunization Schedule. Vaccines are listed under routinely recommended ages. Any dose not given at the recommended age should be given as a "catch-up" immunization at any subsequent visit when indicated and feasible. Italics indicate vaccines to be given if previously recommended doses were missed or given earlier than the recommended minimum age.

Vaccine	Birth	1 mo.	2 mos.	4 mos.	6 mos.	12 mos.	15 mos.	18 mos.	24 mos.	4-6 yrs.	11-12 yrs.	14-16 yrs.
Hepatitis B		Hep B										
			Hep B		Hep B						Hep B	
Diphtheria, Tetanus, Pertussis			DTaP	DTaP	DTaP		DTaP			DTaP	TaD	
H. influenza Type b			Hib	Hib	Hib	Hib						
Polio			IPV	IPV		IPV				IPV		
Measles, Mumps, Rubella						MMR				MMR	MMR	
Varicella (Chicken-pox)						Var					Var	
Hepatitis A						Hep A (in selected states or regions)						

Sources: *Center for Disease Control (www.cdc.gov/nip). Approved by the Advisory Committee on Immunization Practices (ACIP), the American Academy of Pediatrics (AAP), and the American Academy of Family Physicians (AAFP).*

Have you gotten your shots?

Getting immunized is an important aspect to staying healthy. In the United States, routine child-hood vaccinations have drastically reduced the spread of infectious diseases. Ask a parent or teacher to help you check your vaccination record. Use the table on the previous page as a guide. If you find that your vaccinations are not up to date, check with a family doctor or clinic to see if you need to have any "catch-up" immunizations.

To check your records, fill out the spaces below.

Vaccine:	**Dates Vaccinated:**
Hepatitis B	_____
	_____
	_____
Diphtheria, Tetanus, Pertussis	_____
	_____
	_____
	_____
	_____
Tetanus booster	_____
H. influenza Type b	_____
Polio	_____
	_____
	_____
	_____
Measles, Mumps, Rubella	_____
	_____
	_____
Varicella (Chickenpox)	_____
	_____
Hepatitis A (where needed)	_____

Adult Check _____

Initial   Date

Infectious Diseases

Common Cold. The common cold is an illness that everyone will suffer from at least once in their life. Colds are considered a viral infection. They are caused by a virus. There is no known cure for viral infections. Unlike bacteria, viruses are not susceptible to the attacks of antibiotics. The only means of recovery is rest and drinking a lot of fluids. Taking cold medications will only help relieve the symptoms.

Symptoms of the common cold may include runny nose, sneezing, congestion, coughing, sore throat, fever, and achy muscles. If symptoms last longer than two weeks or get increasingly worse, consult with a physician. You might be suffering from something more serious.

Influenza. Influenza, commonly known as "the flu," is also caused by a virus. However, its symptoms are more severe than the common cold. In addition to respiratory difficulties (sneezing, coughing, sore throat), the victim will also suffer from fatigue. If not treated properly, influenza can develop into pneumonia. Pneumonia is a leading cause of death among the sick and the elderly.

Influenza is spread by sneezing or coughing infected droplets into the air. To help control outbreaks of the flu, many Public health care centers offer vaccinations for Types A and B of the virus. The vaccination that you get will boost your immune system for a time. However, the success

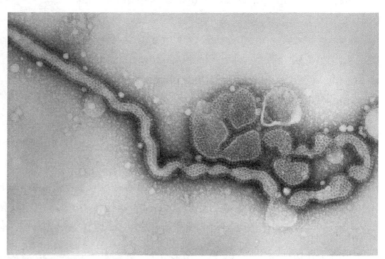

Influenza Type C Virus   *Image courtesy of CDC*

rate is only 60 percent. The elderly and those that come in contact with a lot of people each day, should be vaccinated every year.

Except for severe or high-risk cases (sick and elderly), influenza only needs to be treated with bed rest and fluids. This will enable the body to fight the virus. Muscular pains and fever should be relieved with aspirin or other analgesics. If symptoms do not subside within 10–14 days, contact a physician.

Pneumonia. Pneumonia is a serious condition of the lungs that can lead to death. Pneumonia is usually caused by bacterial or viral infection in the lungs. Symptoms of pneumonia include fever, chest pain, respiratory difficulties, and coughing up yellow-green mucus.

If the case of pneumonia is caused by a bacterial infection, antibiotics may be prescribed to help eliminate the infection. However, if the infection is caused by a virus, rest and fluids might be the only treatment. Severe cases might require the aid of ventilation machines until symptoms subside.

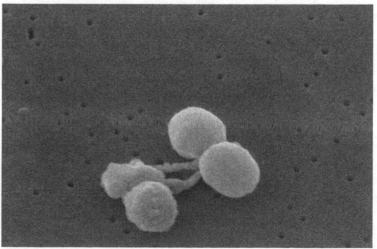

Streptococcus Pneumoniae Bacteria   *Image courtesy of CDC*

Streptococcal Infections. Streptococci are bacteria that can cause diseases such as "strep throat," tonsillitis, pneumonia, and scarlet fever. Streptococci infections are spread by airborne disease-infected droplets. Depending upon the disease, symptoms of streptococcal infections may include fever, enlarged lymph nodes in the neck, sore throat, and fatigue.

Streptococcal infections are usually treated with antibiotics. If not treated properly, streptococcal infections can cause damage to kidneys or develop into rheumatic fever. Rheumatic fever is a very serious condition that can cause damage to the heart.

Hepatitis. Hepatitis is the inflammation of the liver and other tissues. It can be caused by a viral infection. The onset of hepatitis can also be caused by drug abuse or overexposure to a chemical.

Hepatitis can either be acute or chronic. That means, it can either be a temporary illness or it can be a permanent condition. Acute hepatitis can be caused by drug abuse or a virus. Chronic hepatitis is usually the result of a viral infection or an auto-immune disorder.

Viral hepatitis is classified into two groups, Type A and Type B. These distinctions are drawn accord-ing to the known disease-causing agent. Viral hepa-

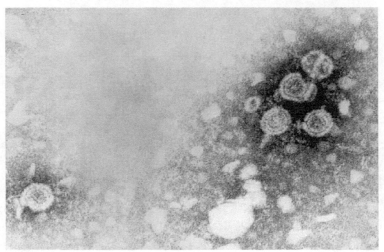

Hepatitis B Virus   *Image courtesy of CDC*

titis, Type A, is generally spread through the fecal contamination of food. This occurs when food is touched by unclean hands. Countries with low standards of hygiene tend to have a high occurrence of hepatitis Type A. Viral hepatitis, Type B, is generally spread through sexual contact and "dirty" needles used by drug abusers.

The symptoms of Type A and B are very similar, except Type B tends to be more severe, causing greater damage to the liver. If any illness is detectable, patients might feel like they have the flu. As the disease progresses, they may become jaundiced as the liver begins to struggle to perform properly.

The treatment for viral hepatitis, acute or chronic, is rest. This allows the body to fight the virus, which cannot be destroyed with medication. Hepatitis that is caused by substance abuse is treated with rest and complete absti-nence from the damaging substance.

Viral hepatitis, Type A, can be avoided by washing your hands after you use the bathroom and only eating at places that conform to the highest standard of culinary hygiene. Before traveling to underdeveloped countries, it might be a good idea to get vaccinated. Viral hepatitis, Type B, can be avoided by abstaining from immoral behavior.

Sexually Transmitted Diseases. Sexually Transmitted Diseases (STDs), also known as venereal diseases, are spread through sexual contact. STDs include syphilis, gonorrhea, chlamydial infections, viral hepatitis, Type B, and gen-ital herpes. The occurrence of STDs tends to be more prevalent in cultures that encourage and endorse immoral lifestyles.

Symptoms of STDs will vary with the disease. They range from mental illness (syphilis) to sterility (gonorrhea) to flu-like symptoms (viral hepatitis, Type B).

STDs that are caused by bacteria are treated with antibiotics. However, some STDs, such as genital herpes and HIV, are caused by a virus and are, therefore, incurable. Symptoms can be relieved but, never eliminated. Some STDs can be life-threatening, such as AIDS and hepatitis.

Vaccinations are now offered for many STDs. But, the best means to avoid the contraction of an STD is to obey God's commands regarding sexual relations. The writer of Hebrews instructs us in this regard by saying, "Marriage is honourable in all, and the [marriage] bed undefiled; but whoremongers [fornicators] and adulterers God will judge" (Hebrews 13:4).

Underline the correct answer.

1.21   The common cold is considered a (**fungal, viral, bacterial**) infection.

1.22   (**Fungal, Viral, Bacterial**) infections cannot be treated with antibiotics.

1.23   The only cure for the common cold and the flu is (**antibiotics, rest, cold medication**).

1.24   Symptoms of the (**flu, common cold**) include sneezing, coughing, sore throat, and fatigue.

1.25   The spread of influenza can be prevented by covering your mouth and nose when you sneeze or cough and by getting (**vaccinated, rest, the cold**).

1.26   Pneumonia is usually caused by a bacterial or viral infection in the (**lungs, nose, throat**), which causes the patient to cough up yellow-green mucus.

1.27   (**The common cold, Strep throat, Pneumonia**) is a leading cause of death among the sick and elderly.

1.28   Streptococci are (**parasites, bacteria, viruses**) that can cause diseases such as strep throat, tonsillitis, pneumonia, and scarlet fever.

1.29   Streptococci infections are spread by (**casual contact, airborne droplets, vectors**).

1.30   If not treated with (**antibiotics, cold medication, a ventilation machine**) streptococcal infections can cause damage to kidneys or develop into rheumatic fever.

✤   **Answer the following** *true* **or** *false*.

1.31   _____ Hepatitis is the inflammation of the liver and other tissues that can be caused by a viral infection or drug abuse.

1.32   _____ Chronic hepatitis is usually caused by drug abuse.

1.33   _____ Hepatitis that is caused by drug use is classified into two groups, Type A and Type B.

1.34   _____ Type A hepatitis is usually contracted by eating food that has been touched by dirty hands.

1.35   _____ Type B hepatitis is usually spread through sexual contact and sharing "dirty" needles.

1.36   _____ Hepatitis can cause severe liver damage, if not treated properly.

1.37   _____ STDs are spread through casual contact.

1.38   _____ Symptoms of STDs are usually never detectable or life-threatening.

1.39   _____ The best means to avoid being infected by a STD is to abstain from fornication and adultery.

Non-Infectious Diseases

As mentioned above, non-infectious diseases are caused by heredity, lifestyle, and the environment. They are usually not the result of exposure to a disease-causing microorganism. Some common non-infectious diseases include heart disease, cancer, and diabetes.

Circulatory System Diseases. Diseases affecting the circulatory system are the leading cause of death among American adults. Circulatory system diseases can either be **congenital** or the result of an unhealthy lifestyle.

Congenital Heart Disease. Congenital heart disease is a malformation of the heart present at birth. It can be caused by rubella in the mother. But, usually there is no known cause for its development. Symptoms of the disease include breathlessness, blue skin (caused by lack of oxygen in the blood), susceptibility to fatigue, and stunted physical development. Many congenital heart conditions can be corrected with surgery.

Coronary Heart Disease. Coronary heart disease is the most common circulatory system disease. Damage to the heart is caused by reduced blood flow to the heart resulting from blocked or narrowing coronary arteries. Narrowed or blocked arteries are caused by the build up of fatty deposits.

Coronary heart disease usually goes unnoticed until chest pain is felt or a heart attack occurs. Chest pain results when the blood flow to the heart is reduced. During exertion, the pain can spread to the arms and neck. The pain is generally dull and is relieved with rest. A heart attack occurs when the blood flow is completely cut off. Heart attacks are usually preceded by dull chest pain that becomes more intense as the muscle struggles to keep blood flowing. Heart attacks can also cause weakness, sweating, and nausea.

Coronary heart disease and its symptoms can be treated with drugs or surgery. Chest pain caused by narrowing of the arteries can be relieved by taking nitrates. Nitrates widen blood vessels, allowing blood to flow more efficiently. Surgical procedures such as coronary artery bypass surgery and angioplasty may also be used to improve blood flow.

Blocked or Constricted Arteries

The best means to prevent the development of coronary heart disease is to eat nutritious foods and exercise regularly. Eating foods that are high in vitamins and minerals will help prevent the unhealthy build up of fat in the walls of main arteries. Regular exercises will keep your heart strong and enable you to deal more effectively with stress, which could constrict blood flow.

Cancer. Cancer is a disease characterized by the unrestrained growth of abnormal cells on or in tissues of the body. The symptoms of cancer are the result of cancer cells draining normal cells of vital nutrients. There are several hundred diseases that can be classified as cancer. Three main categories exist: sarcomas, carcinomas and lymphomas. Sarcomas affect connective tissue, supportive tissue, and blood vessels. Carcinomas affect the skin and tissues that cover or line the organs. Lymphomas affect the tissues of the lymphatic system.

Cancer is caused by the transforming effect of carcinogens on normal cells. Carcinogens are cancer-causing agents. Carcinogens can be chemical (tobacco), physical (asbestos) or biological (virus or fungi). When a normal cell is transformed into a cancer cell, it can multiply rapidly, hampering the health of the surrounding cells.

Depending upon the tissues that are affected, symptoms will vary. However, there are some general warning signs to look out for, such as unexplained weight loss over a short period of time, frequent headaches, coughing up blood, persistent pain in the abdomen, a bleeding mole, blood in urine or feces, and lumps or changes in sex organs.

Treatment for cancer usually involves surgery and some form of radiation therapy or chemotherapy. Radiation therapy tries to destroy abnormal cells by directing radioactive rays through the patient's skin to the diseased tissue. Chemotherapy seeks to

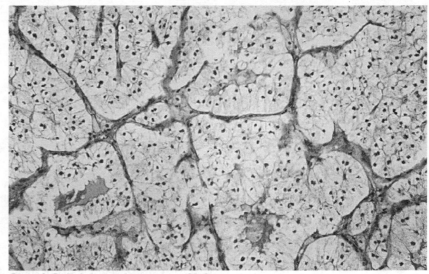

Renal Cell Adenocarcinoma, Kidney   *Image courtesy of CDC*

destroy abnormal cells by injecting anticancer drugs directly into the affected tissue. Because chemotherapy also destroys normal cells, it can cause painful side effects.

Like many non-infectious diseases, cancer and its causes are not fully understood. Therefore, taking certain measures to avoid its occurrence is not always a guarantee. However, avoiding known carcinogens will help keep your body from developing abnormal cells. For example, cigarette smoking is the leading cause of lung cancer. Choosing not to smoke will reduce the risk of developing lung cancer.

Fill in the blanks.

1.40   Congenital heart disease is a malformation of the _____ present at birth.

1.41   Symptoms of _____ heart disease include blue skin, breathlessness, susceptibility to fatigue, and stunted physical growth.

1.42   Congenital heart disease can be corrected with _____ .

1.43   _____ heart disease is the result of reduced blood flow to the heart caused by the build up of fatty deposits in the arteries.

1.44   Coronary heart disease can lead to a _____ .

1.45   Coronary heart disease and its symptoms can be treated with _____ or surgery.

1.46   _____ and good _____ is the best means to prevent the development of coronary heart disease.

Matching.

1.47 _____ a disease characterized by the unrestrained growth of abnormal cells on or in tissues of the body

1.48 _____ a cancer that affects the connective tissue, supportive tissue, and blood vessels

1.49 _____ a cancer that affects the skin and tissues that cover or line the organs

1.50 _____ a cancer that affects the tissues of the lymphatic system

1.51 _____ cancer-causing agents that transform normal cells into cancer cells

1.52 _____ a type of therapy used to destroy abnormal cells by directing radioactive rays at the diseased tissue

1.53 _____ a type of therapy that destroys cells by injecting anticancer drugs directly into the affected tissue

a. chemotherapy

b. carcinogens

c. carcinoma

d. cancer

e. lymphoma

f. radiation

g. sarcoma

Diabetes. Diabetes mellitus is the third most common non-infectious disease among American adults. It is a disease of the pancreas in which insulin is not produced in the correct amounts so that glucose (sugar) can be converted into energy or stored as fat. Diabetes mellitus is categorized into two types: insulin-dependent and non-insulin-dependent. Insulin-dependent is also known as Type I diabetes or childhood diabetes. Type I diabetes usually develops in people between the ages of 9 and 16. Type I diabetes is generally thought to be caused by an inherited predisposition to pancreas problems brought on by a viral infection.

Non-insulin-dependent diabetes is also known as Type II diabetes or adult-onset diabetes. It is also thought to be an inherited predisposition. It is usually brought about by obesity.

Symptoms of diabetes, either Type I or Type II, may include excessive thirst and urination. These symptoms are a result of the body's need to rid itself of excess amounts of glucose in the bloodstream. Excess amounts of glucose in the bloodstream will cause parts of the brain to shut down, which can eventually lead to death.

Type I diabetes is mainly treated with regular insulin injections. These injections may be received one to four times a day. The injection might be administered with an insulin pen or with a portable pump that has a catheter inserted into the skin. In order to help keep insulin levels near normal, Type I diabetics are expected to follow a time-regulated, low-carbohydrate diet and exercise regularly. Type II diabetics are treated with a similar routine of diet and exercise.

To avoid the development of Type II diabetes, you should maintain healthy eating habits and exercise regularly. This will help keep the level of glucose in your bloodstream at normal levels, enabling your pancreas to produce the sufficient amount of insulin needed without overexertion. It is also good to check your family history for diabetes. If there is a possibility that you could be predisposed to diabetes, you should be extra careful to maintain a normal weight through diet and exercise.

If you suspect that you might have diabetes, get tested by your doctor immediately. Untreated diabetes can cause irreversible damage to your eyes, nerve fibers, and kidneys. Blindness, caused by damage to the retina, is one of the complications that can result from untreated diabetes.

Underline the correct answer.

1.54 (**Cancer, Diabetes, Coronary heart disease**) is a disease of the pancreas in which insulin is not produced in the correct amounts so that glucose can be converted into energy or stored as fat.

1.55 (**Type I, Type II**) diabetes usually develops during adolescence and is thought to be caused by an inherited predisposition to pancreas problems.

1.56 (**Type I, Type II**) diabetes is mainly treated with insulin injections, which are received several times a day.

1.57 Both Type I and Type II diabetics can help keep their insulin levels near normal by following a strict diet that is low in (**protein, fat, carbohydrates**).

1.58 Untreated diabetes can cause (**reversible, irreversible**) damage to your eyes, nerve fibers, and kidneys.

Major Diseases – Infectious and Non-Infectious

Fill out the tables below, using information from the text.

Infectious Diseases			
Disease	*Transmission*	*Symptoms*	*Treatment*
Common Cold			
Hepatitis, Viral			
Influenza			

Non-Infectious Diseases

Disease	Possible Causes	Symptoms	Treatment
Cancer			
Coronary Heart Disease			
Diabetes, Type I			
Diabetes, Type II			

Adult Check _____

Initial   Date

Disease Prevention

Medicine. Medicine is man's greatest weapon against disease. It is defined as the art and science of treating and preventing human disease. The science of medicine lies in the knowledge of the human body, medical procedures, and effective treatments. The practical application of this knowledge is the art of medicine.

Over the last two centuries, medicine has made incredible advances towards becoming more of a science than an art, making it much safer and more reputable. The invention of the microscope, for example, shed much light on the cause and spread of infectious diseases. This consequently led to the development of vaccines and other reliable preventative measures.

Health Care. Health care is the actual practice of medical knowledge. It fights disease by encouraging the use of preventative measures, educating people on the dangers of disease and injury, and providing reliable medical care. In industrialized countries, health care is offered and promoted by health care facilities and public health agencies.

Health Care Facilities. Health care facilities include doctor's offices, hospitals, health clinics, nursing homes and hospices.

When you visit a doctor's office, you get highly personalized health care for a fee. Your doctor examines you for specific symptoms and prescribes a treatment that, in his personal knowledge of you, would most likely bring about a cure.

Health clinics also offer health care for a fee, but without the level of personal care that patients receive from a doctor in private practice. Health clinics usually consist of a group of health care professionals that are employed by a corporation.

Hospitals offer round the clock care for people that are recovering from surgery or a life-threatening illness. They also provide emergency services, special treatments, and testing services for those that are on an out-patient status. In the United States, hospitals are either run by the government, business corporations, religious institutions, or communities.

Nursing homes provide health care for the aging, the disabled, and the chronically ill. Depending upon the type of nursing home, different levels of care are provided for residents. Some nursing homes allow residents to be very independent. Other nursing homes offer extended intensive care.

Hospices provide specialized care for the dying. It is the goal of the hospice staff to make the last days of a patient as peaceful as possible. A hospice may be located in a hospital or in a separate building. To increase the level of comfort, hospice nurses will also administer care in the patient's home.

Health Care Professionals. Health care facilities are staffed by physicians, physician assistants, nurses, dentists, and dental hygienists.

Physicians are responsible for the diagnosis and treatment of disease and injury. Treatment may come in the form of prescription drugs, a change in lifestyle, or surgery. Physicians that diagnose and treat common illnesses and injuries are known as primary care physicians. For example, your family doctor is a primary care physician. He or she is qualified to treat common maladies. However, if you contract a disease that requires advanced knowledge, your primary care physician will refer you to a specialist. A specialist is trained in a specific area of medicine. For example, an oncologist is a doctor that specializes in the diagnosis and treatment of cancer.

Physician assistants (PAs) are a relatively new profession in the field of medicine. PAs help alleviate the workload of primary care physicians. However, the role of PAs is distinct from that of nurses. PAs are licensed to examine patients and prescribe treatments.

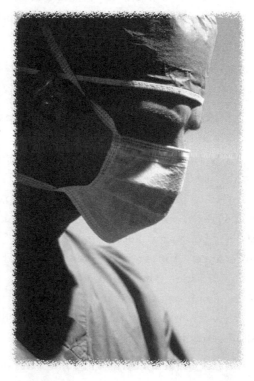

Registered nurses (RNs) are licensed to treat patients and record their symptoms. Like physicians, nurses can specialize in a specific area of medicine. For example, surgery nurses have special training in assisting surgeons. Nurse practitioners, similar to PAs, are licensed to examine patients and render basic care. Licensed practical nurses (LPNs) administer care under the supervision of physicians and RNs.

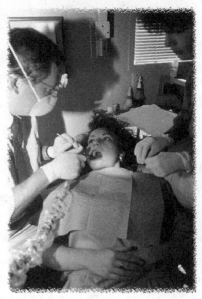

Dentists are responsible for the diagnosis and treatment of diseases affecting teeth or gums. Like physicians, dentists can specialize in a specific area of medicine. For example, orthodontists specialize in the prevention and correction of abnormally spaced teeth.

Dental hygienists assist dentists in the promotion of healthy teeth and gums. Some of their duties include cleaning teeth, educating patients on proper dental hygiene, and assisting the dentist during oral surgery.

Public Health. It is only within the last century that the branch of medicine known as public health has been officially recognized. However, the concern for the health of entire populations has existed for thousands of years. In addition to the writings of the ancient Greeks and Romans, the Old Testament draws a connection between unsanitary living conditions and the spread of disease. The laws regarding personal and community conduct not only set the Israelites apart as holy, they also kept them healthy.

Whether ancient or modern, public health systems seek to promote the health of an entire community by controlling the spread of disease. In most developed countries today, this is accomplished by providing reliable and sanitary systems of waste disposal and ensuring adequate supplies of clean water. Secondly, public health systems seek to provide immunization programs and educate people on the means of disease prevention.

In the United States, public health is a concern for both state and federal officials. State, county, and city governments work together to provide clean water and dispose of waste properly. Some local governments also provide educational and immunization programs to help promote public health.

Federal agencies, such as the Department of Health and Human Services (HHS) regulate and manage government services that promote public health and welfare. Within the HHS, there are eight divisions devoted to public health: Centers for Disease Control and Prevention (CDC), National Institutes of Health (NIH), Food and Drug Administration (FDA), the Substance Abuse and Mental Health Services Administration, the Health Resources and Services Administration, the Indian Health Administration, the Agency for Toxic Substances and Disease Registry, and the Agency for Health Care Policy.

CDC in Atlanta, Georgia   *Image courtesy of CDC*

The Center for Disease Control and Prevention is the main agency concerned with tracking outbreaks and developing methods to combat the spread of disease. Two of the CDC's most effective means of disease control are education and immunization. The CDC often works with local officials to provide certain socio-economic groups with free immunization programs. Its education programs for health workers help to improve public knowledge about disease control and prevention.

The National Institutes of Health (NIH) is the main agency responsible for the discovery and spread of medical information that is pertinent to the control and prevention of disease. NIH consists of 13 institutes of health and the National Library of Medicine. The institutes are staffed by medical professionals and scientists that are working towards finding cures for diseases such as cancer, AIDS, and the common cold.

The Food and Drug Administration is another important division of HHS. It is the responsibility of the FDA to ensure the purity and safety of food products, cosmetics, and pharmaceuticals. The FDA also monitors food labeling to ensure its truthfulness.

Short answer.

1.59   Define medicine. _____
_____
_____

1.60   What type of health care facility offers the most personalized medical care? _____
_____

1.61   What is the difference between a hospice and a nursing home? _____
_____
_____

1.62   What is the role of a physician? _____
_____
_____

1.63   What can a PA do that a RN cannot? _____
_____

1.64   What is the role of a dentist? _____
_____

Answer the following *true* **or** *false.*

1.65   _____   Public health systems seek to promote the health of an entire community by controlling the spread of disease.

1.66   _____   Proper waste disposal and clean water are the primary means of promoting public health.

1.67   _____   In the United States, the Center for Disease Control and Prevention (CDC) is the main federal agency for the promotion of public health and welfare.

1.68   _____   National Institutes of Health (NIH) is the government agency concerned with tracking outbreaks and developing methods to combat the spread of disease.

1.69   _____   The FDA promotes public health by providing free immunization programs and educating health workers.

ACTIVITY

Mission of Mercy: Visiting the Sick

Doctors and nurses are not the only people that can help the sick. You can help someone that is sick or infirm by visiting them. Visiting the sick shows that you care.

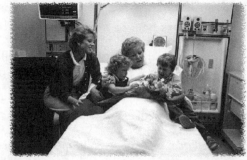

Make a list of three people that you know are sick. Categorize them according to place of recovery/rest. For instance, make a category of people who are recovering in a hospital. Make another category for people you know in a nursing home. Maybe you know someone who is recovering at home or is receiving hospice care. Because nursing home patients tend to need the most encouragement, make them a priority. People that are staying in a hospital, but have received few visitors, should also take top priority.

Before visiting, call the person or a family member to make sure that it is okay for you to visit. Ask if there are any particular needs that you can help with. If not, try to bring a small gift that the sick person will enjoy. It can be a basket of flowers, a book, or a favorite meal. The most important gift that you can bring is a caring disposition. Be sensitive to the needs of the sick person. Listen to them if they want to talk. Talk or read to them if they need to be comforted. Or just sit and hold their hand if that will help them feel better.

"Then shall the King say unto them on his right hand, Come, ye blessed of my Father, inherit the kingdom prepared for you from the foundation of the world: For I was an hungered, and ye gave me meat: I was thirsty, and ye gave me drink: I was a stranger, and ye took me in: Naked, and ye clothed me: I was sick, and ye visited me: I was in prison, and ye came unto me.…Verily I say unto you, Inasmuch as ye have done it unto one of the least of these my brethren, ye have done it unto me" (Matthew 25:34–36, 40).

Fill in the information below regarding your three separate visits:

1. Name:_____

    Illness/condition:_____

    Gift offered:_____

    Particular needs to pray for:_____

    _____

2. Name:_____

    Illness/condition:_____

    Gift offered:_____

    Particular need to pray for:_____

    _____

3. Name:_____

    Illness/condition:_____

    Gift offered:_____

    Particular need to pray for:_____

    _____

Review the material in this section in preparation for the Self Test. The Self Test will check your mastery of this particular section. The items missed on this Self Test will indicate specific areas where restudy is needed for mastery.

SELF TEST 1

Answer the following questions with short answers (each answer, 2 points).

1.01   When was the only time mankind has ever experienced perfect health?_____

_____

_____

1.02   What were the moral and physical ramifications of the Fall of man?_____

_____

_____

1.03   What are six categories of harmful microorganisms?

a. _____   b. _____

c. _____   d. _____

e. _____   f. _____

Match the following items (each answer, 2 points).

1.04 _____ the improper functioning of the body brought about by heredity, infection, diet, or the environment

1.05 _____ cannot be spread through contact or any mechanism of transmission

1.06 _____ caused by the spread of harmful microorganisms

1.07 _____ caused by the multiplication of a small infectious agent which invades a host cell and then destroys it

1.08 _____ caused by the reproduction of a small infectious agent which produces poisons that destroy cells

1.09 _____ caused by the multiplication of fungal organisms on or in the body

1.010 _____ caused by microscopic parasites

1.011 _____ a disease characterized by the unrestrained growth of abnormal cells on or in tissues of the body

1.012 _____ a cancer that affects the connective tissue, supportive tissue, and blood vessels

1.013 _____ a cancer that affects the skin and tissues that covers or lines the organs

1.014 _____ a cancer that affects the tissues of the lymphatic system

1.015 _____ cancer-causing agents that transform normal cells into cancer cells

1.016 _____ a type of therapy that destroys cells by injecting anticancer drugs directly into the affected tissue

a. bacterial infection

b. carcinogens

c. carcinoma

d. cancer

e. chemotherapy

f. disease

g. fungal infection

h. infectious disease

i. non-infectious disease

j. lymphoma

k. protozoan infection

l. sarcoma

m. viral infection

Complete the following sentences using the words above. (each answer, 2 points).

1.017   The _____ immune system consists of the skin, protective secretions, the inflammatory response, and phagocytes.

1.018   _____ are white blood cells that eliminate the chances of infection.

1.019   The _____ immune system is activated if the innate immune system is unable to control the infection.

1.020   _____ immunity depends upon the production of disease specific antibodies to destroy harmful bacteria.

1.021   _____ immunity uses helper cells and killer cells to identify and destroy abnormal cells.

1.022   The contraction of infectious diseases can be avoided by practicing good _____ , avoiding contact with _____ , and boosting your immune system with _____ .

1.023   _____ heart disease is a malformation of the heart present at birth.

1.024   _____ heart disease is the result of reduced blood flow to the heart caused by the build up of fatty deposits in the arteries.

1.025   Coronary heart disease can lead to a _____ .

1.026   _____ and good _____ is the best means to prevent the development of coronary heart disease.

Underline the correct answer (each answer, 2 points).

1.027   (**Fungal, Viral, Bacterial**) infections cannot be cured with antibiotics.

1.028   The only cure for the common cold and the flu is (**antibiotics, rest, cold medication**).

1.029   Symptoms of the (**flu, common cold**) include sneezing, coughing, sore throat, and fatigue.

1.030   Pneumonia is usually caused by a bacterial or viral infection in the (**lungs, nose, throat**), which causes the patient to cough up yellow-green mucus.

1.031   Streptococci are (**parasites, bacteria, viruses**) that can cause diseases such as strep throat, tonsillitis, pneumonia, and scarlet fever.

1.032   Streptococci infections are spread by (**casual contact, airborne droplets, vectors**).

1.033   (**Cancer, Diabetes, Coronary heart disease**) is a disease of the pancreas in which insulin is not produced in the correct amounts so that glucose can be converted into energy or stored as fat.

1.034   (**Type I, Type II**) diabetes usually develops during adolescence and is thought to be caused by an inherited predisposition to pancreas problems.

1.035   (**Type I, Type II**) diabetes is mainly treated with insulin injections received several times a day.

1.036   Both Type I and Type II diabetics can help keep their insulin levels near normal by following a strict diet that is low in (**protein, fat, carbohydrates**).

1.037   Untreated diabetes can cause (**reversible, irreversible**) damage to your eyes, nerve fibers, and kidneys.

Answer the following questions with *true* **or** *false* (each answer, 1 point).

1.038   _____ Hepatitis is the inflammation of the liver and other tissues that can be caused by a viral infection or drug abuse.

1.039   _____ Viral hepatitis, Type A is usually contracted by eating food that has been touched by dirty hands.

1.040   _____ Hepatitis can cause severe liver damage if it is not treated properly.

1.041   _____ Symptoms of STDs are usually never detectable or life-threatening.

1.042   _____ The best means to avoid being infected by an STD is to abstain from fornication and adultery.

1.043   _____ Public health systems seek to promote the health of an entire community by controlling the spread of disease.

1.044   _____ Proper waste disposal and clean water are the primary means of promoting public health.

1.045   _____ In the United States, the Center for Disease Control and Prevention (CDC) is the main federal agency for the promotion of public health and welfare.

1.046   _____ The FDA promotes public health by providing free immunization programs and educating health workers.

Score _____

Adult Check _____

Initial   Date

79 / 99

25

II. DRUG USE AND ABUSE

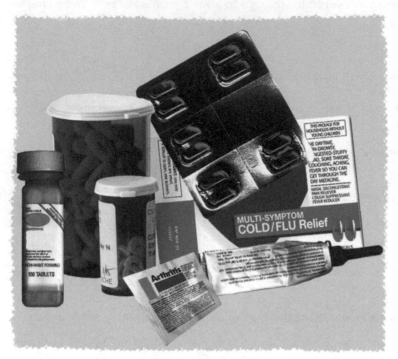

In many people's minds, the term "drug user" conjures up imagines of abuse and misuse. However, a person that uses drugs is not necessarily a criminal. For example, when you have a runny nose or a cough, you usually take some type of cold medicine. When you have a headache, you take aspirin or a non-aspirin pain reliever, right? If so, technically, you could be termed a "drug user." Considering the cultural stigma tied to the word "drug," this might be a little confusing. However, it helps to illustrate a point—if used properly, certain drugs can help maintain health.

By definition, a drug is a chemical substance used to treat, prevent, or diagnose a disease or alter one or more functions of the body. Certain drugs, such as antihistamines and analgesics, can help you feel better when you are sick. Some drugs, such as antibiotics, can help your body fight disease more effectively. While others can be psychologically and physically addictive, such as cocaine.

Whether legal or illegal, drugs can be misused and abused. Understanding the effects of certain substances on the body will help you to distinguish between drug use that is helpful and drug use that is harmful.

Drugs

Most drugs are produced in a laboratory by either altering or combining natural or artificial substances. This allows for greater control over the potency and safety of a particular drug. For example, thyroid hormone can be derived naturally from animal sources. The potency of naturally occurring thyroid hormones can be difficult to control. Thyroid hormones from one animal might be stronger than another source. However, when thyroid hormone is synthesized in a laboratory, it is produced at calculated levels of potency. In addition to being safer, synthesized drugs are more cost effective.

Drug Functions. In order for a drug to work properly, it must be administered properly. Methods of administration may depend upon the illness, the potency of the drug, and the length of treatment. Drugs are administered in several ways. They are taken by mouth (pills), they are injected directly in the bloodstream or tissue (vaccines), they are applied topically (creams), or they are inhaled (nasal sprays).

Once a drug is administered, it is distributed to affected sites via the bloodstream. Enroute to the affected sites, the drug is broken down into a form that can be used by the body or discarded. This process is called metabolism. Metabolism usually occurs in the liver.

Packing Polio Vaccine   *Image courtesy of CDC*

After a drug undergoes metabolism, it interacts with cells or disease-causing agents in a specific way. The interaction either stimulates or blocks a chemical reaction. The effectiveness of a drug depends upon its dosage. Too little or too much interaction of a drug with cells or infecting agents will either render the drug useless or cause it to be harmful. For example, if you have a headache and you decide to take a dosage that is less than is suggested by the manufacturer, your symptoms will probably not go away. In order for the drug to cause the desired response, more of it needs to be taken in order to interact with a greater number of affected cells. However, taking too much of a drug can also cause unwanted effects. Overdosing on drugs as seemingly harmless as aspirin can have fatal effects. Take drugs only in accordance to a doctor's prescription or what is directed on the label.

Drug Classifications. There are several ways to categorize drugs. They can be classified according to name (aspirin, for example), chemical make up (corticosteroids); the disorder they treat (antidepressants), or their specific effect on the body or a disease (stimulants), which is the usual means of classification. Below are just a few categories that drugs can be placed in.

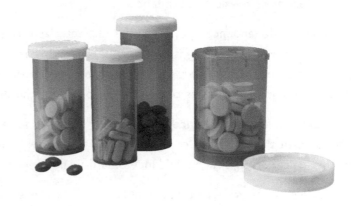

Antibiotics. Antibiotic drugs are one of the most commonly prescribed drugs. They are used to treat bacterial infections. Antibiotics fight invading bacteria by either slowing their multiplication or destroying them. Antibiotic drugs are chosen according to the place of infection and the type of bacteria. If taken for extended periods, antibiotic drugs can harm the immune system by killing "good" bacteria. Penicillin is an example of an antibiotic drug.

Analgesics. Analgesics are commonly known as painkillers. They come in two forms: non-narcotic and narcotic. Non-narcotic analgesics are used for the treatment of mild pain, fever, or swelling. They work by stopping the transmission of pain impulses to the brain and spinal cord or by preventing the perception of pain. Non-narcotic analgesics, such as aspirin, acetaminophen, and ibuprofen can be dispensed over the counter (without prescription).

Narcotic analgesics are used for the treatment of severe pain. They contain opium and natural or synthetic derivatives of opium. Narcotic analgesics kill pain by blocking impulses at specific receptor sites of the brain and spinal cord. Because narcotic analgesics contain opium, a drug that can cause addictive euphoric effects, they can only be dispensed by prescription. Some examples of narcotic analgesics include codeine and morphine.

Diuretics. Diuretic drugs help the body to eliminate excess amounts of water in the blood, tissues, or organs by increasing the production of urine. Diuretics are used to treat fluid build up caused by congestive heart failure, joint injury, cirrhosis of the liver, and kidney disease. They are also used to prevent further complications associated with high blood pressure. Diuretics work by either increasing the volume of blood flow through the kidneys or by limiting the kidney's ability to put water and sodium back into the blood.

Tranquilizers. Tranquilizers are used to help treat mental disorders by producing a calming effect. Tranquilizers can be categorized into two groups: anti-anxiety drugs and anti-psychotic drugs. Anti-anxiety drugs are prescribed to help relieve the physical and emotional symptoms of anxiety. They work by slowing brain activity and reducing the heart rate. Valium® is an example of an anti-anxiety drug.

Anti-psychotic drugs are used to treat severe mental disorders such as schizophrenia. Anti-psychotic drugs work by blocking the effects of certain neurotransmitters on the brain. Neurotransmitters are chemicals that relay messages from one nerve cell to another. Dopamine is a neurotransmitter that is associated with psychotic behavior. Anti-psychotic drugs, such as Lithium, can control the activity of dopamine.

Hormones. Endocrine drugs (hormones) treat disorders of the endocrine system. The endocrine system consists of hormone-producing glands that regulate the body's functions, metabolism, and growth. Endocrine drugs correct the level of specific hormones in the body. For example, insulin is an endocrine drug. When a person takes insulin, he or she is increasing the level of insulin in their body. This is meant to correct the underproduction of insulin by the pancreas. Other endocrine drugs include growth hormones, synthroid, and estrogen.

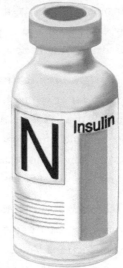

Drug Abuse. Drug abuse is the taking of a legal or illegal drug in a manner that can cause physical harm or psychological and physical dependence.

People usually abuse drugs because they enjoy the physical or emotional effects that the drug produces. Depending upon the drug and its dosage, the experience can be very intense or rather mild. The continued need or desire for these experiences can lead to psychological or physical dependence.

Physical dependence upon a drug is characterized by a state of mental and physical abnormality when the drug is withdrawn. The body has become so accustomed to the presence of the drug that it cannot function properly without it. Usually, the abuser needs greater and greater dosages of the drug in order for the drug to have its desired effect.

Psychological dependence is marked by a craving for the drug. Abusers rely on the elated state that the drug causes in order to deal with the problems they might face. Psychological or physical dependence on a drug usually leads to an addiction to the drug.

Drugs or medications that are either purchased over the counter or prescribed by a doctor are just as susceptible to abuse as those substances that are controlled by the government or forbidden by law, such as heroin and marijuana. If you take a medication that has not been prescribed for your use, you are abusing the drug. Your use of it could quite possibly cause you harm. It could also cause you to become psychologically or physically dependent upon it. For example, medications that contain codeine are highly addictive.

Fill in the blanks.

2.1   A _____ is a chemical substance used to treat, prevent, or diagnose a disease or alter one or more functions of the body.

2.2   Most drugs are produced in a _____ by either altering or combining _____ or artificial substances.

2.3   Drugs are either administered orally, by injection, applied _____ , or inhaled.

2.4   After a drug is administered, it undergoes the process of _____ .

2.5   During metabolism, the drug is _____ down into a form that can be used by the body or discarded.

2.6   A drug causes an effect by either _____ or blocking a chemical reaction by a cell or a disease-causing agent.

2.7   The effectiveness of a drug depends upon its _____ .

2.8   Drugs can be classified according to _____ , _____ make-up, the disorder it treats, or specific effects on the body.

2.9   _____ drugs fight invading bacteria by either slowing their multiplication or destroying them.

2.10   _____ stop the transmission of pain impulses to the brain and spinal cord or by preventing the perception of pain.

2.11   _____ kill pain by blocking impulses at specific receptor sites of the brain and spinal cord.

2.12   _____ drugs help the body to eliminate excess amounts of water in the blood, tissues, or organs by increasing the production of urine.

2.13   _____ drugs produce a calming effect by slowing brain activity and reducing the heart rate.

2.14   _____ drugs block the effects of certain neurotransmitters on the brain.

2.15   _____ drugs correct the level of specific hormones in the body.

True or false.

2.16   _____ Drug abuse is the taking of any drug in a manner that can help bolster one's physical or psychological state.

2.17   _____ People commonly abuse drugs because they enjoy the physical or emotional effects that the drug produces.

2.18   _____ Physical dependence upon a drug is characterized by a craving for the drug.

2.19   _____ Psychological dependence is marked by a state of mental and physical abnormality when the drug is withdrawn.

2.20   _____ Only illegal drugs can be used in such a way that causes physical harm or psychological and physical dependence.

Commonly Abused Drugs. Any drug can be abused. Drugs that are commonly abused can be placed into six categories: hallucinogens, stimulants, narcotics, depressants, inhalants, and steroids.

Hallucinogens. Hallucinogens are naturally-occurring or synthetically-produced drugs that can cause hallucinations. Hallucinogens have no medical use. They are often used for their relaxation or "out of body" feelings and are termed recreation drugs. LSD, marijuana, psilocybin, and PCP are types of hallucinogens. Because of their dangerous psychological and physical effects, hallucinogens are outlawed in the United States.

Marijuana is the most widely abused drug in the U.S. Marijuana is the dried leaves, stems, and flowering tops of the hemp plant Cannabis Sativa. THC (tetrahydrocannabinol) is the active ingredient in marijuana. It causes users to feel as if they are in a conscious dreamlike state. THC can be absorbed by the body through smoking, eating the leaves, or by drinking tea made with marijuana. The leaves are usually smoked in the form of a joint. Marijuana is not physically addicting; however, it can lead to psychological dependence. People who use the drug to lessen feelings of depression actually become more depressed. Marijuana inhibits the brain from processing information. Users of marijuana have a more difficult time processing and remembering information. Continued use of marijuana increases these problems. Marijuana use is illegal in the United States except in some states where medical use has been legalized.

LSD also known as "acid" is another often used hallucinogen drug. LSD is generally taken by mouth and alters people's perceptions of reality. The effects of LSD use are unpredictable. The drug brings about intense feelings, sensations, and dramatic mood shifts. These experiences, known as "trips," can be pleasant or bad. "Bad trips" can evoke feelings of terror and panic. Trips can also cause dizziness, nausea, and weakness. The occurrence of "bad trips" is unpredictable. "Flashbacks" might even occur several months or years after a trip. LSD use is also linked to long term mental illness.

Just as today, early Christians were confronted by the challenges of living in a sinful world. They too faced pressure from their peers and the difficulties of taking a stand for Christ. The city of Rome was filled with all types of temptations for a believer. The apostle Paul wrote the letter of Romans to encourage these Christians. "I beseech you therefore, brethren, by the mercies of God, that ye present your bodies a living sacrifice, holy, acceptable unto God, which is your reasonable service. And be not conformed to this world: but be ye transformed by the renewing of your mind, that ye may prove what is that good, and acceptable, and perfect, will of God" (Romans 12:1-2). In this LIFEPAC you are using your mind to learn about different types of drugs. You then need to make choices based on what you learned on how to correctly use or avoid different types of drugs. Paul also reminds Christians that their bodies are to be living sacrifices to God. Just as offerings are gifts to God so are the bodies of believers.

Stimulants. Stimulants increase the activity of the central nervous system. They can make a user feel more alert and less hungry. Adverse side effects include heart palpitations, nervousness, hallucinations, and seizures. Some well-known substances that can be classified as stimulants include methamphetamines and cocaine.

Methamphetamines or "meth" is a highly addictive stimulant. A person can become addicted to the drug after one use. Methamphetamines produce high levels of dopamine. The production of dopamine in the brain makes people feel pleasure. When a person feels happy or receives a reward, the dopamine areas of the brain are triggered. Methamphetamines mimic this feeling of pleasure but only for a short time. Interestingly "meth" actually damages the brain cells which naturally produce dopamine. This increases the chances of addiction to the drug. Methamphetamines increase heart rate, decrease appetite and cause memory loss. Long term methamphetamine use rots a user's teeth.

Cocaine is derived from the leaves of the South American plant known as coca. It was first used in the European countries as a local anesthetic. Depending upon its form, cocaine can be inhaled through the nostrils, injected into the bloodstream, or smoked with a special pipe. Its use can easily lead to cardiac arrest and psychological dependence. Like methamphetamines, cocaine is highly addictive. Cocaine can give a person feelings of power and control. Prolonged use results in paranoia and depression. When combined with alcohol, cocaine has devastating affects on the body. Because of its harmful effects, cocaine is a strictly controlled substance in the United States.

Narcotics. Narcotics are mainly pain-killing drugs that are derived from opium. Narcotics, such as morphine and codeine, are prescribed by doctors to relieve severe forms of pain. The feeling of euphoria that narcotics produce can be highly addictive. Even if they are prescribed by a doctor, narcotics should be used with great caution.

Morphine is one of the most widely abused narcotics. It is usually prescribed for pain involving serious injury or surgery. The drug can also cause feelings of euphoria. Its long-term use can lead to physical and psychological addiction.

Heroin, a derivative of morphine, is an illegal substance. It is sold on the street as a white powder that can be inhaled through the nostrils, mixed with water and injected into the veins, or smoked in a special pipe. Heroin provides a quick rush followed by wakeful and drowsy states. It also causes feelings of peace, warmth, and indifference. Long-term use can cause physical and psychological addiction, along with increased tolerance for the drug. The heroin addict needs increasingly larger doses of the drug to get the same results. Using contaminated needles often spreads diseases such as AIDS and Hepatitis B. Heroin overdose often leads to death. More illegal drug deaths are cause by heroin than any other drug.

People using illegal drugs spend a great deal of money for their addiction. While costs of the different drugs vary, the amount of money spent on illegal drugs adds up over time. All of this money could be better spent on things which are useful and do not harm the body. The Bible recognizes that people often spend their money unwisely. Isaiah 55:2 states, "Wherefore do ye spend money for that which is not bread? and your labour for that which satisfieth not? hearken diligently unto me, and eat ye that which is good, and let your soul delight itself in fatness." Not only does the Bible warn people not to spend money unwisely, but it also promises that the wise will be rewarded. Care for your body in ways that will provide life-long blessings and not short-term satisfaction.

Depressants. Depressants reduce or slow activity of the central nervous system. They act as a sedative, causing the user to feel relaxed or drowsy. They are often prescribed to relieve anxiety or insomnia. If taken in combination with other depressants (such as alcohol), they can cause coma or death. Examples of depressants include barbiturates and tranquilizers, which can be physically addictive if taken for long periods.

Barbiturates are derived from barbituric acid. They suppress brain activity by blocking the ability of nerves in the brain to send or receive signals. Barbiturates have been used to treat anxiety, sleeping disorders, and epilepsy. However, widespread abuse has decreased the use of barbiturates as a medication. If used for more than four weeks, barbiturates can cause serious withdrawal symptoms. When taken with other depressants, barbiturates can be deadly.

Rohypnol or "roofies" is a drug whose use is associated with teens and students of college age. People who use this drug become immediately relaxed for about four hours. Often they have no idea of what happened to them during this time. Other side effects include vomiting, seizure, and coma. Unfortunately, some people give rohypnol to unsuspecting people to take advantage of them. This is often done by pouring rohypnol powder in a drink. Teens need to be careful when going to large events only to drink things which they have poured or opened themselves. A young person should not leave a drink unattended because someone could slip rohypnol in the drink. When going to public events, especially ones which are not carefully supervised, it is always best to stay with a group of friends who will encourage and watch out for one another.

Inhalants. Often time when people think of illegal drugs, they do not consider household items which can be misused as drugs. Another way some teens find to get "high" is through using seemingly harmless items. Users inhale or "huff" items like paint thinner, gas, glue, spray paint, and hair spray. The goal is to get a few moments of artificial happiness. There are great dangers in inhaling these household products including the slowing of body functions such as the heart rate. Nerve and brain damage can also occur as a result of this behavior. Additionally inhaling these items does not allow enough oxygen to enter the blood stream. Heat failure and death can follow as a result misusing items meant for other purposes.

Paint thinner and hair spray were not invented to be inhaled by people. The people who invented the products were trying to solve problems or needs they saw. Similarly, God did not create people to misuse their bodies. In fact, God created people in his own image. When people remember that God created them in his likeness, it should affect the way they care for their bodies. Ephesians 2:10 says, "For we are his workmanship, created in Christ Jesus unto good works, which God hath before ordained that we should walk in them." Not only as God's image bearers are people to care for their bodies, but they are also to do good to others in the name of Jesus.

Anabolic Steroids. Anabolic steroids or steroids are used to increase muscle and bone mass. The word anabolic means to build muscle. Doctors rarely prescribe anabolic steroids to their patients. Only when all other options have failed might a doctor recommend that a person with anemia or severe weight loss from cancer take the drug.

Anabolic steroids are an illegal drug of choice for athletes or others wanting to quickly gain muscle bulk or weight. Users of steroids take doses far higher than any doctor would ever prescribe to even the sickest patient. Some people turn to steroids as a quick alternative to lifting weights and training. Others are unsatisfied with their physical build or body type and try to become larger through steroids. Ironically, young people who use steroids may stunt their growth.

Like other drugs, steroids have devastating side effects. High blood pressure, severe acne, and liver failure can result from steroid use. Probably the most well-known side effects are mood swings. Steroid users can experience intense rage, paranoia, and depression.

In looking at the devastating impact of steroids, Christians are reminded again that each person is created in the image of God. In the very beginning of scripture in Genesis 1:26 God says, "Let us make man in our image, after our likeness: and let them have dominion over the fish of the sea, and over the fowl of the air, and over the cattle, and over all the earth, and over every creeping thing that creepeth upon the earth." Believers often read this verse and think of the dominion people are to have over God's creation. They do not always remember that they too are part of God's creation. God's people are to care for their bodies which are part of God's creation. Using illegal substances which harm the body does not show care for what God has created. It also shows dissatisfaction with the way in which God made them. Instead, God calls his people to care for their bodies just as they care for His creation.

Matching.

2.21 _____ increases the activity of the central nervous system

2.22 _____ increases the heart rate and suppresses the appetite

2.23 _____ first used by Europeans as a local anesthetic, now abused for its euphoric effects

2.24 _____ can cause extreme rage and paranoia

2.25 _____ reduces the activity of the central nervous system

2.26 _____ suppresses brain activity by blocking the ability of nerves in the brain to send or receive signals

2.27 _____ reduces the physical and psychological symptoms of anxiety by reducing brain activity

2.28 _____ pain killing drugs that are derived from opium

2.29 _____ prescribed for pain involving serious injury or surgery

2.30 _____ illegal derivative of morphine that is sold on the street as a white powder

2.31 _____ naturally-occurring or synthetically-produced drugs that can cause hallucinations

2.32 _____ can evoke feelings of terror and panic

2.33 _____ causes user to experience a conscious dreamlike state

a. amphetamines

b. barbiturates

c. steroids

d. cocaine

e. depressants

f. hallucinogens

g. heroin

h. LSD

i. marijuana

j. morphine

k. narcotics

l. stimulants

m. tranquilizers

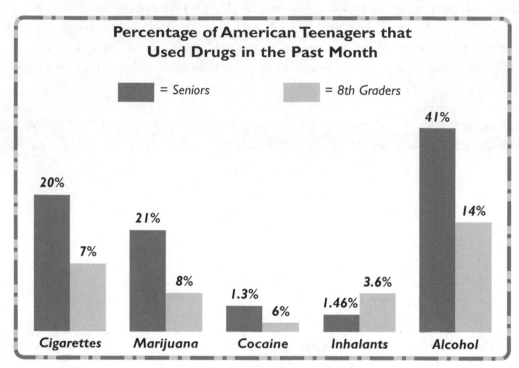

Source: National Institute on Drug Abuse. Monitoring the Future Study. Annual surveys. U.S. Health 2010.

High School

Health

five

LIFEPAC TEST

80 / 100

Name _____

Date _____

Score _____

LIFEPAC TEST UNIT 5

Answer *true* **or** *false* (each answer, 1 point).

1. _____ God commanded mankind to rule over the environment.

2. _____ The cultural mandate to "subdue" the environment does not permit mankind to use natural resources without regard for future generations.

3. _____ The best means to avoid being infected by an STD is to abstain from fornication and adultery.

4. _____ Vaccinations and education programs are the primary means of promoting public health.

5. _____ Physical dependence is marked by a state of mental and physical abnormality when the drug is withdrawn.

6. _____ Drug abuse is the taking of any drug in a manner that can cause psychological or physical dependence.

7. _____ Christians will no longer be troubled by disease when they are vaccinated.

8. _____ Drunkenness is considered a sin because it is pleasurable.

9. _____ Medicine is the art and science of treating and preventing disease.

10. _____ Waste is deposited into incinerators in thin layers which are then compacted and covered with soil.

Matching (each answer, 2 points).

11. _____ the layer of the atmosphere that the ozone layer is part of

12. _____ the type of wastes that can be broken down by other organisms into a reusable form

13. _____ the type of wastes that are solid, liquid, or gas wastes that are toxic, flammable, corrosive, reactive, or radioactive

14. _____ the process by which certain waste materials, such as plastic, glass, aluminum, and paper are prepared for reuse

15. _____ the addictive drug found in tobacco

16. _____ a disease frequently developed by smokers and passive smokers

17. _____ a disease of the pancreas in which insulin is not produced in the correct amounts so that glucose can be converted into energy or stored as fat

18. _____ formed in the atmosphere when chemicals, called volatile organic compounds (VOCs), and nitrogen dioxide (NO_2) are acted upon by sunlight

19. _____ when burned, it can cause an increase of CO_2, ozone, and sulfur dioxide in the atmosphere

a. biodegradable

b. cancer

c. diabetes

d. fossil fuel

e. hazardous

f. nicotine

g. ozone

h. recycle

i. stratosphere

j. thermosphere

k. exosphere

Underline the correct answer (each answer, 3 points).

20. Levels of (**CO₂, oxygen, VOCs**) in the atmosphere can be reduced by increasing the use of nuclear power and by planting trees in urban areas.

21. (**Thermal inversion, photochemical smog, industrial smog**) prevents the dissipation of pollutants by normal air currents.

22. High levels of ozone in the atmosphere can cause (**thermal inversion, photochemical smog, industrial smog**), which can trigger respiratory problems.

23. Sulfur dioxide is a main component of (**thermal inversion, photochemical smog, industrial smog**).

24. The contraction of infectious diseases can be avoided by practicing good (**hygiene, nutrition**), avoiding contact with (**carcinogens, vectors, phagocytes**), and boosting your immune system with immunizations.

25. The (**innate, adaptive**) immune system consists of the skin, protective secretions, the inflammatory response, and phagocytes.

26. The (**innate, adaptive**) immune system consists of cellular immunity and humoral immunity.

27. (**Coronary, Congenital**) heart disease is the result of reduced blood flow to the heart caused by the build-up of fatty deposits in the arteries.

antibiotics	carcinogens	hallucinogens	steroids	stimulants
cancer	depressants	humoral immunity	rest	tranquilizers
	disease	hydrological cycle	sewage	

Using the word list above, fill in the following blanks (each answer, 3 points).

28. The _____ is the continuous movement of water between the Earth's surface and the atmosphere.

29. The leading cause of water contamination in countries without water treatment plants is improperly managed _____ .

30. _____ depends upon the production of disease specific antibodies to destroy harmful bacteria.

31. _____ increase the activity of the central nervous system.

32. _____ reduce the activity of the central nervous system.

33. _____ are sometimes used by athletes to increase muscle mass.

34. _____ fight invading bacteria by either slowing their multiplication or by destroying them.

35. _____ reduce the physical and psychological symptoms of anxiety by reducing brain activity.

36. _____ are naturally occurring or synthetically produced drugs that can cause hallucinations.

37. _____ is the improper functioning of the body brought about by heredity, infection, diet or the environment.

2

38.	_____ is a disease characterized by the unrestrained growth of abnormal cells on or in tissues of the body.

39.	The only cure for the common cold and the flu is _____ .

Multiple choice (each answer, 2 points).

40.	What makes up all of the living and nonliving things that surround and support you? _____
	a.	the atmosphere
	b.	the soil
	c.	the troposphere
	d.	the environment

41.	What condition is characterized by the inflammation of the liver and other tissues that can be caused by a viral infection or drug abuse? _____
	a.	diabetes
	b.	STD
	c.	CFC
	d.	hepatitis

42.	What type of infection cannot be treated with antibiotics? _____
	a.	viral
	b.	bacterial
	c.	protozoan
	d.	fungal

43.	What was the motivating factor behind Theodore Roosevelt's conservationist ideas? _____
	a.	to preserve the health of mankind
	b.	to preserve the forests
	c.	to conserve water
	d.	to recycle plastic

44.	What type of immunity uses helper cells and killer cells to identify and destroy abnormal cells? _____
	a.	congenital
	b.	humoral
	c.	cellular
	d.	innate

45.	In the United States, what is the main federal agency for the promotion of public health and welfare? _____
	a.	Center for Disease Control and Prevention (CDC)
	b.	Department of Health and Human Services (HHS)
	c.	National Institute of Health (NIH)
	d.	Food and Drug Administration (FDA)

Alcohol

Alcohol is the most commonly abused depressant. It is also known as ethanol or ethyl alcohol. It is a colorless liquid that is produced by the fermentation of sugars by yeast. Ethyl alcohol is found in beer, wine, and hard liquor.

Alcohol has been created throughout history wherever fruits and grains have been grown. The people of the Near East made wine from grapes. The ancient Egyptians used barley to make beer. The Medieval Scots used the whole grain of wheat to make whiskey. Alcohol, particularly wine, was a drink that could be trusted because it destroyed disease-causing agents so often spread by drinking water or milk.

Though the process of alcohol manufacturing has become more sophisticated over the years, the fermentation process has basically remained the same. Fermentation occurs when yeast converts carbohydrates found in grains or juice into ethyl alcohol and carbon dioxide. A similar process of fermentation occurs when milk is allowed to sour. Souring, the change in taste and smell that you detect when a container of milk is allowed to sit out on the counter overnight or go unused after the expiration date, is the result of the growth of bacteria. The bacteria form lactase, which acts as the yeast does in the fermentation of alcohol. Lactase converts the milk sugars to an acid known as lactic acid. The effects of drinking sour milk and alcohol, however, are very different.

Effects. As a depressant, alcohol slows nerve activity. If ingested in excessive amounts, it can have toxic effects. As with any drug, the body's response depends upon the dosage. The initial effects of drinking alcohol may include reduced anxiety, increased confidence, loosened inhibitions, and a sense of well being. As more alcohol is consumed, the effects will become more intense. Reduced anxiety might turn into drowsiness. Increased confidence and loosened inhibitions might lead to foolish behavior, such as drunk driving, which could endanger the lives of others.

Alcohol increases the flow of gastric juices in the stomach, thus aiding in the relief of indigestion. Doctors throughout the centuries have used alcohol to treat many ailments. In ancient times, wine was used to treat stomach ailments. Today, some doctors encourage patients that struggle with anxiety or stress to drink a glass of wine every day. The sedative effect of alcohol helps to relieve tension. But alcohol can lead to other severe health problems, such as high blood pressure and cardiac arrest. Drinking fermented grape products may reduce the level of cholesterol in the bloodstream.

From a physical or moral standpoint, consuming large amounts of alcohol is never good. The Bible contains strict commands against drunkenness and warns against its destructive effects. In Ephesians 5:18, Christians are told to not become drunk, but to be filled by the Spirit. In Galatians 5:19–22, drunkenness is included in a list of the "works of the flesh," among which adultery, murders, and idolatry are also named.

Drunkenness can have mild to severe physical consequences, depending upon the amount of alcohol that is consumed. These effects can range from dehydration to death. As a diuretic, alcohol causes the body to urinate more frequently. Depending upon the amount of alcohol that is consumed, a certain level of dehydration will occur.

Dehydration caused by overindulgence in alcohol can cause a number of bodily discomforts that are collectively known as a "hangover." A hangover is characterized by headache, pain behind the eyes, nausea, and dizziness. The discomforts are mainly caused by a decrease in the level of fluids surrounding the brain. Drinking certain types of alcohol, such as brandy and whiskey, can cause more severe hangovers. The only cure for a hangover is rest and drinking plenty of water.

Some more severe physical consequences of drunkenness include extreme disorientation, coma, and death. Extreme disorientation and confusion occurs when the amount of alcohol in the blood is high enough to severely impair the functioning of the central nervous system. The brain's activity is so retarded that simple tasks such as standing and talking become difficult.

If the level of alcohol in the blood is increased after this point, certain body systems are in danger of being shut down. When blood alcohol levels reach a certain point, the central nervous system is no longer able to properly regulate the functioning of the respiratory or circulatory systems. The overwhelming sedative effect of the alcohol will cause the drunkard to first fall asleep and then slip into a coma. Death can result if the blood alcohol level is high enough to stop the functioning of the respiratory system altogether.

Another leading cause of death related to drunkenness is drunk driving. People usually drive drunk because the alcohol gives them a heightened sense of confidence. They believe that they are able to drive safely when they are, in fact, a danger to themselves and others. Alcohol consumption is a leading contributor to motor vehicle accidents.

Alcohol Dependence. Alcohol dependence, commonly known as alcoholism, is a condition characterized by the habitual and gluttonous consumption of alcohol. Doctors and scientists are not actually sure what causes alcohol dependence. However, several factors are thought to contribute to its development: psychological condition, social environment, euphoric effects of alcohol, genetic make-up, and spiritual condition.

Alcohol dependence usually takes several years to develop. Through continual reinforcement, the drinker learns to depend upon alcohol to deal with psychological stress. The alcohol becomes a means of escape that is readily available. Symptoms of an increasing dependence upon alcohol might include a strong desire to become intoxicated when stressful situations arise, the need to have alcohol available at all times, and the tendency to socialize in the company of other heavy drinkers.

Dependence begins with an increasing tolerance for the drug. As the alcoholic consumes more and more alcohol with regularity, the liver adapts by processing the drug at a quicker rate. In order for the alcoholic to achieve a certain level of drunkenness, he or she must drink more and more. This is known as the law of diminishing returns.

As the dependence increases, the alcoholic experiences a loss of control over his or her drinking habits. More alcohol is needed more frequently, both psychologically and physically, in order to function normally. However, the drinking is often done despite adverse physical and social effects, such as liver damage and abusive behavior.

The most serious state of alcoholism is characterized by constant drinking. The drinker continues to drink in order to avoid symptoms of withdrawal. Withdrawal symptoms include mental and physical disorders such as shaking, hallucinations, and convulsions.

During any of these stages, the alcoholic might decide to quit drinking. Unless alcoholics have been renewed by the power of the Holy Spirit, however, they often return to their destructive habits as a means of escape and comfort.

Physical and Psychological Effects of Alcoholism. The Book of Proverbs imparts much wisdom on the subject of drinking. To warn against the dangers of alcoholism, it gives clear and honest descriptions of the physical and psychological state of the alcoholic. For example, Proverbs 23:29–35 reads:

> "Who hath woe?
> who hath sorrow?
> who hath contentions?
> who hath babbling?
> who hath wounds without cause?
> who hath redness of eyes?
> They that tarry long at the wine;
> they that go to seek mixed wine.
> Look not thou upon the wine when it is red,
> when it giveth his colour in the cup,
> When it moveth itself aright.
> At the last it biteth like a serpent,
> and stingeth like an adder.
> Thine eyes shall behold strange women,
> and thine heart shall utter perverse things.
> Yea, thou shalt be as he that lieth down in the midst of the sea,
> or as he that lieth upon the top of a mast.
> They have stricken me, shalt thou say, and I was not sick;
> they have beaten me, and I felt it not:
> When shall I awake? I will seek it yet again."

The alcoholic can develop severe emotional problems. As the Proverb explains, he or she can be plagued by sorrow and discontent. The alcohol, which the alcoholic looks to as a cure, only compounds his or her problems. This growing frustration with self and others often manifests in changes in behavior and personality. For example, the person that was once self-controlled and peaceable might suddenly become irritable and abusive. There is a high rate of suicide among alcoholics.

The physical symptoms of alcoholism might include flushed facial skin, poor overall health, stomach and intestinal pain in the morning, tingling in the legs and hands, confusion, and irregular pulse. These symptoms usually indicate the development or the existence of irreversible damage to body tissues. Some alcohol-related disorders include cancer of the mouth, tongue, and esophagus, cirrhosis of the liver, hepatitis, coronary heart disease, stroke, ulcers, kidney failure, and brain damage. Pregnant women who consume alcohol run the risk of miscarriage or, if they carry their babies to term, a birth defect known as fetal alcohol syndrome.

Alcohol and the Christian. The Bible contains many remarks regarding the use of alcohol. Its availability and use is described as the fruits of honest labor (Deuteronomy 14:26, Ecclesiastes 9:7); a means to make one's heart glad and relieve sorrow (Judges 9:13, Psalm 104:15, Proverbs 31:6–7); a remembrance of things to come (Matthew 26:27–29); and as a remedy for physical ailments (1 Timothy 5:23).

However, the Bible also contains commands regarding its abuse. For example, Ephesians 5:18 states, "And be not drunk with wine, wherein is excess; but be filled with the Spirit." Drunkenness is characteristic of the unsaved. "Now the works of the flesh are manifest, which are these; Adultery, fornication, uncleanness, lasciviousness, idolatry, witchcraft, hatred, variance, emulations, wrath, strife, seditions, heresies, envyings, murders, drunkenness, revellings, and such

37

like: of the which I tell you before, as I have also told you in time past, that they which do such things shall not inherit the kingdom of God" (Galatians 5:19–21). Drunkenness indicates a desire to find peace in the things of the world rather than in God.

In addition to the restriction against drunkenness, the Bible also tells us that those that believe drinking is not a sin should not do so to the detriment of another. No form of eating or drinking should be done if it causes another to stumble. This can be avoided by abstaining from alcoholic drinks in the presence of those that struggle with alcoholism and those that believe drinking to be a sin (Romans 14:14–23). "We then that are strong ought to bear the infirmities of the weak, and not to please ourselves. Let every one of us please his neighbour for his good to edification" (Romans 15:1–2).

The Effects of Blood Alcohol Levels. Blood Alcohol Levels (BAL) are measured in milligrams percent of alcohol per 100 milliliters of blood. For example, a BAL of .10 indicates that 1/1000 of your blood consists of alcohol.

BAL is affected by the individual's gender, weight, and rate of consumption. For example, a 120-pound woman that has 2 glasses of wine in a two-hour period will have a BAL of .08. However, a man of the same weight that drinks the same amount of alcohol in the same amount of time will have a significantly lower BAL.

BAL	Observable Effects
.02	Mellow feeling, flushed face, talkativeness.
.05	Noticeable relaxation, less alert, reduced self-control, slightly impaired coordination.
.08	Drunk driving limit. Definite judgement and coordination impairment.
.10	Unpredictable displays of emotion, slurred speech, slowed reactions.
.15	Clearly drunk. Very disoriented and confused.
.30	Unconsciousness may occur.
.40	Death possible for some; many lose consciousness.
.50	Risk of death very high. Many stop breathing.

*Source: **www.habitsmart.com** website, "Understanding Blood Alcohol Level"*

Short answer.

2.34 What is alcohol made from? _____

2.35 What are some of the medicinal uses of alcohol? _____

_____

2.36 What are some of the physical consequences of drunkenness? _____

_____

_____

2.37 Why is drunkenness considered a sin? _____

_____

2.38 Briefly, describe the physical and psychological state of the alcoholic: _____

_____

_____

_____

_____

 **Interview on Alcohol Use**

As a teenager, it is important to consider the thoughts and experiences of others. It will help you to gain the understanding and wisdom needed to make important choices. The Bible describes the value of wisdom as such:

> "Happy is the man that findeth wisdom,
> and the man that getteth understanding;
> For the merchandise of it is better than the merchandise of silver,
> and the gain thereof than fine gold.
> She is more precious than rubies:
> and all the things thou canst desire are not to be compared unto her.
> Length of days is in her right hand;
> and in her left hand riches and honour.
> Her ways are ways of pleasantness,
> and all her paths are peace.
> She is a tree of life to them that lay hold upon her:
> and happy is every one that retaineth her" (Proverbs 3:13–18).

The choices that you make today will affect the rest of your life. That is why it is vitally important to hear what respectable adults have to say about important issues such as alcohol use.

In this activity, you will interview three adults that are active Christians. They can be family members, fellow church members, family friends, or even teachers. Using the following questions, get their understanding and wisdom on alcohol use. Conclude the activity by answering the questions under "Your Thoughts."

Interview #1:

Name of interviewee: _____

Age: _____

Occupation: _____

Relationship to interviewer: _____

Questions:

1. Have you ever drank alcohol? If so, why? _____

   _____

   _____

2. Do you think it is wrong to drink alcohol? Why or why not? (Ask for the Scriptural basis of their answer.)

   _____

   _____

   _____

3. Why do you think alcohol is so widely abused? _____

   _____

   _____

Interview #2:

Name of interviewee: _____

Age: _____

Occupation: _____

Relationship to interviewer: _____

Questions:

1. Have you ever drank alcohol? If so, why? _____

   _____

   _____

2. Do you think it is wrong to drink alcohol? Why or why not? (Ask for the Scriptural basis of their answer.)

   _____

   _____

   _____

3. Why do you think alcohol is so widely abused? _____

   _____

   _____

Interview #3:

Name of interviewee: _____

Age: _____

Occupation: _____

Relationship to interviewer: _____

Questions:

1. Have you ever drank alcohol? If so, why? _____

_____

_____

2. Do you think it is wrong to drink alcohol? Why or why not? (Ask for the Scriptural basis of their answer.)

_____

_____

_____

3. Why do you think alcohol is so widely abused? _____

_____

_____

Your Thoughts:

After you finish interviewing the three adults, answer the questions below.

1. What did you learn about alcohol use that you didn't already know? _____

_____

_____

2. How might the information that the interviewees passed along help you to make decisions about alcohol in the future? _____

_____

_____

_____

Adult Check   _____

              Initial   **Date**

Tobacco

Tobacco is a plant that is grown for its leaves and stems. The leaves and stems contain an addictive drug known as nicotine, which can have various effects on the body. The leaves are either dried or smoked and then processed for use in cigarettes, cigars, and pipes, chew, and snuff. Cigarettes are the most widely used form of tobacco.

Tobacco was first introduced to Western culture by Christopher Columbus. While exploring the Americas in 1492, Columbus encountered the Arawak Indians. The Arawaks used tobacco for medicinal and religious purposes. The Indians believed that tobacco had a healing power. The Europeans continued to use it mainly as a medicine until the seventeenth century when it became popular for its pleasurable effects. In the American colonies, the growth and sale of tobacco brought much-needed capital.

Tobacco was first smoked in pipes and cigars and snuffed in a finely ground form. Cigarettes were not widely used until the latter part of the nineteenth century. The invention of a machine that could inexpensively roll the cigarettes boosted popular demand.

By the beginning of the twentieth century, cigarettes were an inextricable part of American culture. Movie stars were seen smoking on screen and off. The cigarette break was a much anticipated part of the day for factory workers and doctors alike. During World War II, cigarettes were supplied to U.S. soldiers as part of their rations.

It was not until the 1960s that medical studies began to reveal a link between tobacco use and various forms of cancer. However, despite reports put out by the American Cancer Society and the government's insistence that tobacco products carry a warning label, the number of tobacco users in the United States is still surprisingly high. Over 50 million Americans smoke cigarettes, cigars, and pipes.

Effects. The harmful effects of tobacco use are mainly caused by nicotine, tar, and carbon monoxide. The nicotine in tobacco can enter the bloodstream by being smoked, chewed, or snuffed. Nicotine is an addictive substance that acts as a stimulant. As a stimulant, nicotine speeds up nerve activity by increasing the body's production of epinephrine, a hormone produced by the adrenal glands. Epinephrine can increase the heartbeat and blood pressure and open up air passages. Nicotine is also known to cause an opposite effect. It can act as a tranquilizer, slowing the heart rate.

Because of its highly addictive properties, nicotine can cause adverse effects if tobacco usage is stopped. Withdrawal symptoms usually occur within 24 hours. Symptoms might include a craving for tobacco, headaches, anxiety, fatigue, and irritability.

The thousands of harmful chemicals found in tobacco are collectively known as tar. Tar is a dark, sticky substance that irritates the organs of the respiratory system. The mouth, throat, and lungs respond to the presence of tar particles by increasing the production of mucus. The excess mucus can have both helpful and harmful effects. As intended, the mucus keeps irritants away from vulnerable tissues. However, the regular production of excess mucus can also cause damage to the lining of the lungs.

The inhalation of tar also causes damage to the tiny sacs in the lungs, called alveoli. Alveoli are responsible for the absorption of oxygen into the bloodstream. When alveoli are damaged, levels of carbon monoxide in the blood are increased and the levels of oxygen are decreased. In order to compensate for the deficiency of oxygen in the blood, the lungs and the heart work harder. This can cause shortness of breath and an increased heart rate.

Carbon monoxide is one of the poisonous gases that are produced by the burning of tobacco leaves. When inhaled, it is detrimental to the absorption of oxygen. Consistently high levels of carbon monoxide in the blood can cause circulatory problems, which may culminate in heart disease.

Smoking is related to nearly 400,000 deaths each year. It is a leading cause of diseases affecting the respiratory and circulatory systems. When compared to nonsmokers, smokers more frequently develop chronic bronchitis, lung cancer, heart disease, and emphysema.

Smoking is also harmful to the unborn. If a mother smokes, there is a greater chance that her baby will be born prematurely and/or underweight. Smoking retards the proper development of the child while in the womb. A parent's smoking habits can also slow the growth of a child after it has been born. The child, in effect, is a "passive smoker." He or she inhales the smoke without actually puffing on a cigarette.

Passive smokers are at as great of a risk as smokers for respiratory and circulatory diseases. In particular, children of smokers tend to develop disorders such as asthma, ear infections, and pneumonia more frequently. A recent study concluded that passive smokers are twice as likely to develop heart disease than those that are not regularly exposed to secondhand smoke.

 Underline the correct answer.

2.39   Tobacco leaves and stems contain an addictive drug known as (**carbon monoxide, tar, nicotine**).

2.40   In the (**1880s, 1960s, 1990s**), medical studies began to reveal a link between tobacco use and various forms of cancer.

2.41   The harmful effects of tobacco use are mainly caused by nicotine, (**tar, alveoli, mucus**) and carbon monoxide.

2.42   As a stimulant, (**nicotine, tar, carbon monoxide**) speeds up neural activity by increasing the body's production of epinephrine.

2.43   Withdrawal symptoms from (**nicotine, tar, carbon monoxide**) addiction include craving for tobacco, headaches, anxiety, fatigue, and a lack of patience.

2.44   (**Nicotine, Tar, Carbon monoxide**) causes damage to the alveoli and increases the production of mucus in the mouth, throat, and lungs.

2.45   (**Nicotine, Tar, Carbon monoxide**) hinders the body's ability to absorb needed amounts of oxygen.

2.46   (**Smokers, Nonsmokers**) more frequently develop chronic bronchitis, lung cancer, heart disease and emphysema than (**smokers, nonsmokers**).

2.47   (**Passive smokers, Nonsmokers, Children**) are at risk as much as smokers for respiratory and circulatory diseases.

Smoking and Health

- ❖ Smoking can retard the growth of healthy lungs.

- ❖ Smoking increases the chances of respiratory illness.

- ❖ Smoking hurts athletic performance.

- ❖ Smoking puts added stress on the heart, causing it to beat more rapidly, even while at rest.

- ❖ Smoking can lead to lung cancer.

- ❖ Smoking can lead to nicotine addiction.

- ❖ Smoking can make good foods taste bad.

- ❖ Smoking can pollute the air with many poisons, causing great harm to others.

- ❖ Smoking can cause others to cough or wheeze.

Source: National Center for Chronic Disease Prevention and Health Promotion. "Facts on Youth Smoking, Health, and Performance" and "Secondhand Smoke Facts."

Smokeless Tobacco. Chewing tobacco and snuff are forms of smokeless tobacco. Chewing tobacco is wadded up into a ball and placed between the gums and cheek or lip. Snuff is inhaled into the nostrils. Both methods of absorption place the tobacco in direct contact with tissues, increasing the risk of cancer in the mouth, nose, or throat. Nicotine can also make smokeless tobacco highly addictive.

Quitting. For the reasons listed above, individuals that use tobacco with regularity should make an effort to stop. However, quitting can be a difficult task. The addiction that often accompanies tobacco use can seem like an impossible foe to defeat. The craving to smoke or chew is not just psychological, it is physical. After months or years of tobacco use, the body becomes physically dependent upon the presence of nicotine. Counseling and support groups can convince the tobacco user that he or she needs to stop, but the persistence to do so must be an individual choice.

The best method of quitting is going "cold turkey." Once the tobacco user decides to stop, he or she must never return to its use. Slowly cutting down on tobacco use is rarely a successful means of quitting. Medical devices, such as nicotine patches or nicotine gum, exist to help the tobacco user cope with withdrawal symptoms.

If you know someone that is trying to quit, encourage them to do so. Tell them that once a person quits, the risk of respiratory or circulatory disease drops dramatically. If the person is a Christian, remind them to call on God for strength to resist the temptation to use tobacco.

Tobacco Use and the Christian. There is no verse in the Bible prohibiting the use of tobacco. However, because tobacco tends to be highly addictive, and because of its harmful effects on the body, it is wise not to use it. I Corinthians 6:12 states, "All things are lawful unto me, but all things are not expedient: all things are lawful for me, but I will not be brought under the power of any." Addiction to any drug, food, or behavior can be a powerful force. Our desires for the substance can make us its slave. As those who have been redeemed by the blood of Jesus, we are to be slaves of righteousness (Romans 6:22). Our actions should be guided by a desire to glorify God, not satisfy our senses. "For ye are bought with a price: therefore glorify God in your body, and in your spirit, which are God's" (I Corinthians 6:20). We are called to care for our bodies in such a way that enables us to serve God to our fullest potential. The psychological and physical disorders that are caused by tobacco use can weaken an individual, preventing him or her from fulfilling the duties that God has called them to do. Habits that unnecessarily destroy the body do not bring glory to God. Avoid the development of such habits.

Answer the following *true* **or** *false*.

2.48 _____ Quitting tobacco use is usually very easy.

2.49 _____ The best method of quitting is to cut the tobacco use gradually.

2.50 _____ Nicotine gum and patches can help tobacco users cope with withdrawal symptoms.

2.51 _____ Addiction to any drug, food, or behavior can make us its slave.

2.52 _____ The psychological and physical disorders caused by tobacco use can weaken an individual, preventing him or her from fulfilling the duties that God has called them to do.

Smoking: A Wise Choice?

Despite the widespread publication of the adverse health effects of smoke, many people, both young and old, choose to smoke. In the last twenty-five years, the demand for cigarettes has actually risen. Over 315 billion cigarettes were sold in the United States in 2009. American teenagers are one of the largest consumer groups. Approximately 20 percent of American teenagers smoke. The question is, if people know that smoking is bad for them, why do they choose to do it?

In this activity, you will analyze the reasons that people give for smoking. Below, list three reasons why people smoke. In the space provided, weigh each reason against the facts. In other words, prove that the reasons **not** to smoke far outweigh the reasons to smoke.

1. Reason: _____

   Opposing Argument/Contradictory Facts: _____

   _____

2. Reason: _____

   Opposing Argument/Contradictory Facts: _____

   _____

3. Reason: _____

   Opposing Argument/Contradictory Facts: _____

   _____

 Adult Check _____

                                             Initial   **Date**

Review the material in this section in preparation for the Self Test. The Self Test will check your mastery of this particular section as well as your knowledge of the previous section.

SELF TEST 2

antibiotics	anti-psychotic	cellular	diuretics	drug	metabolism	non-narcotic
anti-anxiety	broken	coronary	dosage	endocrine	narcotic	stimulating

Complete the following sentences, using the words above (each answer, 2 points).

2.01   A _____ is a chemical substance used to treat, prevent, or diagnose a disease or alter one or more functions of the body.

2.02   After a drug is administered, it undergoes the process of _____ .

2.03   A drug affects the body by either _____ or blocking a chemical reaction by a cell or a disease-causing agent.

2.04   The effectiveness of a drug depends upon its _____ .

2.05   _____ fight invading bacteria by either slowing their multiplication or destroying them.

2.06   _____ analgesics stop the transmission of pain impulses to the brain and spinal cord or by preventing the perception of pain.

2.07   _____ analgesics kill pain by blocking impulses at specific receptor sites of the brain and spinal cord.

2.08   _____ help the body to eliminate excess amounts of water in the blood, tissues, or organs by increasing the production of urine.

2.09   _____ drugs produce a calming effect by slowing brain activity and reducing the heart rate.

2.010   _____ drugs block the effects of certain neurotransmitters on the brain.

2.011   _____ drugs correct the level of specific hormones in the body.

2.012   _____ immunity uses helper cells and killer cells to identify and destroy abnormal cells.

2.013   _____ heart disease is the result of reduced blood flow to the heart caused by the build-up of fatty deposits in the arteries.

Answer the following questions *true* **or** *false* (each answer, 1 point).

2.014   _____ Drug abuse is the taking of any drug in a manner that can help bolster one's physical or psychological state.

2.015   _____ People commonly abuse drugs because they enjoy the physical or emotional effects that the drug produces.

2.016   _____ Psychological dependence is marked by a state of mental and physical abnormality when the drug is withdrawn.

2.017 _____ Only illegal drugs can be used in such a way that causes physical harm or psychological and physical dependence.

2.018 _____ The best method of quitting is to cut the tobacco use gradually.

2.019 _____ Nicotine gum and patches can help tobacco users cope with withdrawal symptoms.

2.020 _____ The psychological and physical disorders caused by tobacco use can weaken an individual, preventing him or her from fulfilling the duties that God has called them to do.

2.021 _____ Hepatitis is the inflammation of the liver and other tissues that can be caused by a viral infection or drug abuse.

2.022 _____ Public health systems seek to promote the health of an entire community by controlling the spread of disease.

Match the following items (each answer, 1 point).

2.023 _____ increases the activity of the central nervous system

2.024 _____ increases the heart rate and suppresses the appetite

2.025 _____ first used by Europeans as a local anesthetic, now abused for its euphoric effects

2.026 _____ causes increased muscle mass

2.027 _____ reduces the activity of the central nervous system

2.028 _____ suppresses brain activity by blocking the ability of nerves in the brain from sending or receiving signals

2.029 _____ reduces the physical and psychological symptoms of anxiety by reducing brain activity

2.030 _____ pain-killing drugs that are derived from opium

2.031 _____ prescribed for pain involving serious injury or surgery

2.032 _____ illegal derivative of morphine that is sold on the street as a white powder

2.033 _____ naturally occurring or synthetically produced drugs that can cause hallucinations

2.034 _____ can evoke feelings of terror and panic

2.035 _____ causes user to experience a conscious dreamlike state

2.036 _____ the improper functioning of the body brought about by heredity, infection, diet, or the environment

2.037 _____ caused by the multiplication of a small infectious agent which invades a host cell and then destroys it

2.038 _____ cancer-causing agents that transform normal cells into cancer cells

a. amphetamines

b. barbiturates

c. steroids

d. carcinogens

e. cocaine

f. depressants

g. disease

h. hallucinogens

i. heroin

j. LSD

k. marijuana

l. morphine

m. narcotics

n. stimulants

o. tranquilizers

p. viral infection

Underline the correct answer (each answer, 2 points).

2.039   Tobacco leaves and stems contain an addictive drug known as (**carbon monoxide, tar, nicotine**).

2.040   As a stimulant, (**nicotine, tar, carbon monoxide**) speeds up neural activity by increasing the body's production of epinephrine.

2.041   Withdrawal symptoms from (**nicotine, tar, carbon monoxide**) addiction include craving for tobacco, headaches, anxiety, fatigue, and a lack of patience.

2.042   (**Nicotine, Tar, Carbon monoxide**) causes damage to the alveoli and increases the production of mucus in the mouth, throat, and lungs.

2.043   (**Nicotine, Tar, Carbon monoxide**) hinders the body's ability to absorb needed amounts of oxygen.

2.044   (**Smokers, Nonsmokers**) more frequently develop chronic bronchitis, lung cancer, heart disease, and emphysema than (**smokers, nonsmokers**).

2.045   (**Passive smokers, Nonsmokers, Children**) are at as great of a risk as smokers for respiratory and circulatory diseases.

2.046   (**Fungal, Viral, Bacterial**) infections cannot be cured with antibiotics.

2.047   (**Cancer, Coronary heart disease, Diabetes**) is a disease of the pancreas in which insulin is not produced in the correct amounts so that glucose can be converted into energy or stored as fat.

Multiple choice (each answer, 2 points).

2.048   The harmful effects of tobacco use are mainly caused by what substances? _____
       a. Nicotine, tar, carbon dioxide
       b. Nicotine, tar, carbon monoxide
       c. Opium, alcohol, carbon monoxide
       d. Nicotine, alveoli, carbon

2.049   What were some of the moral and physical ramifications of the fall of man? _____
       a. spiritual and physical death, disease, pain in childbirth, and the strain of work
       b. physical death and disease, pain in childbirth, and the strain of work
       c. spiritual death
       d. spiritual and physical life

2.050   What is the role of a physician? _____
       a. to treat patients and record their symptoms
       b. to diagnose and treat disease and injury
       c. to diagnose and treat diseases affecting teeth or gums
       d. to assist RNs

Answer the following questions (each answer, 2 points).

2.051   What are the four types of infections?

       a. _____   b._____

       c. _____   d._____

2.052   What are six categories of harmful microorganisms?

       a. _____   b._____

       c. _____   d._____

       e. _____   f._____

Score _____

Adult Check _____

                      Initial   Date

III. HEALTH AND THE ENVIRONMENT

The environment is an important determinant of your health. It consists of all the living and nonliving things that surround and support you. Living environmental factors include such things as plants, animals, and people. Nonliving factors include the air, water, and soil.

God has created the world in such a way that the condition of one factor can greatly affect the condition of another. For example, if harmful chemicals are dumped into a river, the plants in and around the river will not grow properly. And if the plants cannot grow, the animals that depend upon them will die. Both animals and plants feed humans—our healthy existence is dependent upon theirs. That is why when we protect and preserve the environment we are protecting and preserving ourselves.

Environmental Changes

Since the creation of the world, the environment has undergone some dramatic changes. The antediluvian world was very different from the world that we know today. According to some scientists, the waters which were placed "above the firmament" (Genesis 1:6–8) produced a "greenhouse effect" over the entire earth. Temperatures were mild and humidity was very high. According to Genesis 2:5–6, water did not move from the surface of the earth to the atmosphere and then back down to the surface again as it does today. As one scientist has observed, the earth was watered by a diurnal dew system. "For the Lord God had not caused it to rain upon the earth" (Genesis 2:5).

In Genesis 6–8, we have record of the greatest catastrophic event ever to affect the environment. The flood not only changed the atmosphere, instituting the hydrological cycle, but it also changed the structure of the earth's crust.

Water not only poured from heaven, it burst forth from the "fountains of the deep" (Genesis 7:11). As one writer has observed, the change described in chapter 7 implied the occurrence of "volcanic eruptions, earthquakes, and tidal waves," which led to the formation of separated land masses, mountain ranges, and deep canyons.

After the canopy was depleted and the floodwaters receded, the world was no longer a "greenhouse." Newly formed mountain ranges and lower levels of humidity caused the air to circulate, allowing for climate variations. In some regions, heavy snowfall and falling temperatures led to the formation of glaciers. In other regions, heavy cloud cover and volcanic ash caused heavy rains and milder temperatures (Brown).

For many years after the Flood, the environment slowly continued to experience change. The clouds of volcanic ash and heavy precipitation eventually dissipated, allowing for warmer temperatures and increased sunlight. In regions north of the equator, glaciers receded as heavy snowfall and freezing temperatures gradually tapered off, forming the climate that exists today.

The changes that occurred to the environment also affected animal and plant life. Unable to deal with the alterations in climate, many species became extinct. For several generations after the Flood, mankind remained in a climate that was fairly mild. However, after the building of the Tower of Babel, God separated mankind into nations, scattering them into varying regions and climates.

Mankind and the Environment

Man's dispersion had a two-fold purpose. It stopped mankind from achieving unbridled corporate rebellion, and it forced mankind to obey God's command to "replenish the earth and subdue it" (Genesis 1:28).

As has been emphasized throughout this course, God's intended relationship between mankind and the creation was similar to that between a king and his kingdom. As the image bearer of the Creator-King, mankind was intended to tend and keep the creation for God's glory.

Following the earth-rending events of the Flood, mankind's cultural mandate to subdue the environment included the use of animals for food. "And the fear of you and the dread of you shall be upon every beast of the earth, and upon every fowl of the air, upon all that moveth upon the earth, and upon all the fishes of the sea; into your hand are they delivered. Every moving thing that liveth shall be meat for you; even as the green herb have I given you all things" (Genesis 9:2–3).

©Carlyle Calvin

God's gift of all things to mankind, however, did not allow for abuse. The earth and all that dwells within it belongs to God. It is His. Mankind's dominion simply underscores the importance of man in relation to the rest of Creation. As man is subservient to God, so the environment is subservient to mankind.

To our own detriment, mankind has failed throughout history to follow God's direction to "tend and keep" the environment. We have killed certain species of animals out of pleasure rather than need. We have cut down forests and burned fuels without regard for the needs of future generations. We have discarded wastes improperly, ignoring the possible short-term and long-term effects on human life.

As in all things, obedience to God's commands is not only required for God's glory but for our good. Tending and keeping the creation in such a way that conserves natural resources and protects the environment will help to keep us and future generations healthy. However, when we refuse to be good stewards, problems will occur.

Answer the following *true* **or** *false.*

3.1 _____ Your environment consists of all the living and non-living things that surround and support you.

3.2 _____ The catastrophic events surrounding the Flood drastically changed the environment.

3.3 _____ After the Flood, the high humidity produced a "greenhouse effect" over the entire earth.

3.4 _____ God split mankind into nations so that it would "fill the earth and subdue it."

3.5 _____ God intended mankind to be subservient to the environment.

3.6 _____ The cultural mandate to "subdue" the environment allows mankind to use natural resources without regard for future generations.

Air Essentials

The layer of air that surrounds the earth and supports life is called the atmosphere. It is a mixture of gases and particles including oxygen, nitrogen, hydrogen, carbon dioxide, water vapor, and dust.

The atmosphere consists of five layers, each of which varies in temperature, composition, and thickness.

The troposphere is the layer that envelops the earth's surface. All living things exist within the troposphere. The air within the troposphere is moved about by the changing temperature surface of the earth. Weather conditions are, in turn, caused by the circulation of the air. The troposphere is approximately 5 to 10 miles thick.

The stratosphere is the second layer of the atmosphere. It ranges from 5 to 30 miles above the earth's surface. The ozone layer is part of the stratosphere. It protects the earth from the damaging effects of the sun's ultraviolet rays.

The layer that reaches from 30 to 50 miles above the surface of the earth is known as the mesosphere. The temperature range within the mesosphere is markedly colder than the layers below it.

The thermosphere or ionosphere is the fourth layer of the atmosphere. It extends from 50 to 300 miles above the earth's surface. It is called the thermosphere and the ionosphere because of its high temperatures and high content of ions. Meteors are spotted and usually vaporized as they pass through this layer.

The exosphere is the outermost layer. Its outer limits extend 600 miles above the earth's surface.

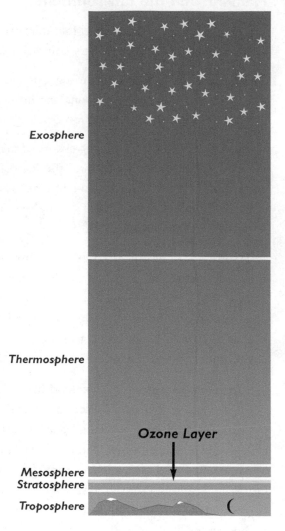

Divisions of the Atmosphere

There are approximately 350,000 cubic miles of water on and surrounding the earth. It is contained in oceans (93 to 97 percent), ice (2 percent), and fresh water (1 percent). Sources of fresh water include rivers, lakes, underground springs, and atmospheric moisture.

Air Pollution. Because clean air is vital to human health, air pollution is a major environmental concern. Air pollution can lead to respiratory problems and aggravate existing respiratory and circulatory diseases. Pollutants in the atmosphere can also cause damage to vegetation and animal life. In order to curb the effect of air pollution on human health and the environment, many countries have enacted laws requiring regions to maintain a specified level of "clean air." Since the passing of the Clean Air Act in 1970 by the United States, levels of pollutants in the air have been reduced in many regions and cities.

The air is polluted by many factors. The burning of fossil fuels for transportation, industry, and domestic purposes all contribute to the introduction of pollutants into the air. Volcanoes, decaying organic material, lightning, and plants also add to the amount of "pollutants" in the air. As one scientist has noted, "the amount of pollutants in the air, particularly sulfates and nitrates, on a global scale comes about equally from natural and human sources."

Types of Air Pollutants. Air pollutants can be categorized into either gases or particulates. Gases that are considered pollutants cause harm to animal or plant life. Some gases that are considered toxic occur naturally in the earth's atmosphere. For example, nitrogen is an essential component of the earth's atmosphere. However, if nitrogen levels in the air rise above normal, the atmosphere can become toxic to animal or plant life.

Particulates are solid or liquid particles that settle after being dispersed in a gas. Particulates enter the body via inhalation or contact with the skin. They also affect the body indirectly through the contamination of food or drink sources. Examples of particulates include lead from automobile exhaust, cigarette ash, pesticides, and dust.

Underline.

3.7   The (**atmosphere, exosphere, mesosphere**) consists of a mixture of gases and particles including oxygen, nitrogen, hydrogen, carbon dioxide, water vapor, and dust.

3.8   All living things exist within the (**troposphere, exosphere, stratosphere**).

3.9   The ozone layer is part of the (**troposphere, exosphere, stratosphere**).

3.10 Air pollution can lead to (**digestive, respiratory, industrial**) problems.

3.11 The air is polluted by (**natural and human, domestic and industrial, organic and aquatic**) sources.

3.12 Air pollution occurs when certain gases or particulates are ejected into the (**ozone layer, atmosphere, sea**).

3.13 (**Gases, Particulates, Toxic fumes**) are solid or liquid particles that settle after being dispersed in a gas.

Carbon Dioxide. The burning of gasoline and other fossil fuels by man has significantly increased the amount of toxic gases and particulates in the atmosphere. Of particular note is the increase of a gas known as carbon dioxide (CO_2). In the last 100 years, CO_2 in the Earth's atmosphere has increased by 25 percent. This is alarming to some because they believe that increased levels of CO_2 will lead to global warming. However, there is no conclusive evidence that the global climate is becoming significantly warmer. In fact, some scientists believe that there actually might be a slight cooling trend.

Increased levels of CO_2 in the atmosphere should, however, be a concern. Though CO_2 levels have varied throughout history, scientists are still uncertain as to the long-term effects of heightened levels of CO_2. Scientists do know that CO_2 is an important "greenhouse gas." It helps maintain the Earth's comfortable climate by preventing the escape of heat radiated from the Earth's surface. It is a natural product of all animal life. It also is produced by decaying vegetation, volcanic eruptions, and forest fires. Secondary to these sources of CO_2 is the burning of fossil fuels. Fossil fuels are primarily used to produce gas for vehicles, heat, and industry.

©Eric Wunrow

Levels of CO_2 can be reduced in a number of ways that will not detract from the quality of modern life. As Dr. Dixy Lee Ray, former chairman of the Atomic Energy Commission, has pointed out, "...we can phase out the use of fossil fuels for making electricity and turn to the established and proven technology that has no adverse impact on the atmosphere—nuclear power." On a national and global level, this would result in an increased use of electricity for heating, transportation, and industrial purposes. An increased number of nuclear power plants would easily meet the increased demand for electricity.

Another practical way to reduce the amount of CO_2 in the atmosphere is to plant trees. Carbon dioxide is used by trees and other plants for photosynthetic activity. The reforestation of urban areas can be especially helpful in reducing the impact of CO_2 emissions by gas-powered vehicles and industry.

Ozone. Ozone is a form of oxygen. It occurs naturally in the Earth's atmosphere. The upper part of the second layer of the atmosphere, known as the stratosphere, consists mainly of ozone. This section of the atmosphere is called the ozone layer. The ozone layer absorbs much of the ultraviolet radiation from the sun's rays, protecting the earth and its inhabitants. Ozone is formed in the stratosphere by the effects of sunlight on oxygen molecules. The thickness of the ozone layer has naturally occurring variations, depending upon seasons and location. "Holes" can appear in the ozone layer but soon disappear or are displaced. Nitrogen in the stratosphere keeps the natural production of ozone within a certain range, sufficient for the support of life on earth.

©Eric Wunrow

Ozone is also formed by the activities of man. It is produced commercially to purify air, water, and certain foods. This is done by sending an electrical discharge through pure, cold oxygen.

The burning of fossil fuels for transportation, industry, and domestic heat is another man-made source of ozone, but only secondarily. Ozone is formed in the atmosphere when chemicals called volatile organic compounds (VOCs) and nitrogen dioxide (NO_2) are acted upon by sunlight. VOCs are ejected into the atmosphere by gas-powered vehicles, chemical refineries, and industrial plants. Vegetation and forest fires also emit VOCs. Nitrogen dioxide is emitted by electrical power plants and motor vehicles.

High levels of ozone in the atmosphere can cause photochemical smog. Photochemical smog can lead to acute or temporary health problems. It can trigger respiratory problems, such as asthma attacks, shortness of breath, and coughing. Heightened amounts of ozone are also known to cause damage to tree growth.

The effects of ozone are particularly noticeable during the occurrence of thermal inversion. Thermal inversion is a natural phenomenon. It occurs when a layer of cool air is trapped underneath a layer of warm air, preventing the dissipation of pollutants by normal air currents. Usually, pollutants are circulated with the upward flow of warm air from the earth's surface. Thermal inversion occurs most frequently in the afternoon when the sunlight is the warmest and brightest. Thermal inversion also occurs more often over areas that are hemmed in by natural barriers such as mountains. Ozone levels, therefore, are highly susceptible to weather conditions. A region might be responsible for the production of chemicals that are favorable to the creation of ozone, but wind or nightfall will remove that threat.

Because ozone sources in the atmosphere are both natural and man-made, it can be difficult to control ozone levels. In areas such as Atlanta, Georgia, for example, there is a great amount of tree growth. Trees—along with motor vehicles, chemical refineries, and industrial plants—produce VOCs and NO_2. Even when pollution from man-made sources was reduced, the region still suffered from high levels of ozone. Reducing ozone in various regions is not always as simple as reducing the burning of fossil fuels, but that can help reduce the concentration of ozone and other pollutants in the atmosphere.

Chlorofluorocarbons. Chlorofluorocarbons (CFCs) have caused a great amount of concern among many environmentalists. CFCs have been blamed for the depletion of ozone in the stratosphere. Chloride is a chemical by-product of CFCs. Chloride apparently contributes to the break-down of ozone in the atmosphere. Consequently, CFC production has been theoretically linked to an increase in the occurrence of skin cancers caused by "holes" in the ozone layer.

Though curtailed in some industries, CFCs are produced and used widely. CFCs are used mainly in refrigeration and air conditioning. CFCs are vital to many industries, including medicine and food. Without the use of CFCs, many foods, such as meat and dairy products, would spoil before they reached your table. Medical supplies, such as vaccines, blood, and organs, could not be used to protect and save the lives of millions of individuals. CFCs are also used in substances that extinguish fire.

The chloride produced by CFCs is found abundantly in nature. It is produced naturally by volcanoes at yearly rates that dwarf the amount produced by man. As one writer has noted, chloride emissions from one major volcanic eruption can produce 200 times the annual amount of chloride produced by CFCs. If chlorides do indeed cause long-term or short-term damage to the ozone layer, then natural pollutants are much to be blamed.

Sulfur Dioxide. Sulfur dioxide is a colorless gas that has an irritating odor. Sulfur dioxide can cause damage in the form of atmospheric gas, dry particles, and acid. When it is combined with water, it becomes sulfuric acid. Sulfur acid is highly corrosive. It can cause damage to stone, metal, wood, and especially flesh.

Sulfur dioxide is a main component of industrial smog. Sulfur dioxide is produced when fossil fuels are burned for transportation, industrial, or domestic heating purposes. It is also the natural product of volcanic eruptions. The production of sulfates by man-made and natural sources are about equal. Sulfur dioxide is blamed for respiratory problems, eye irritations, and highly acidic rain.

✤ Fill in the blanks.

3.14   In the last 100 years, the burning of _____ by man has significantly increased the level of CO_2 in the atmosphere.

3.15   _____ helps maintain the Earth's comfortable climate by preventing the escape of heat radiated from the Earth's surface.

3.16   Carbon dioxide is a natural product of _____ and _____ life.

3.17   Levels of CO_2 in the atmosphere can be reduced by increasing the use of _____ power and by planting _____ in urban areas.

3.18   _____ is formed in the atmosphere when chemicals, called volatile organic compounds (VOCs), and nitrogen dioxide (NO_2) are acted upon by sunlight.

3.19   _____ are emitted into the atmosphere by gas-powered vehicles, chemical refineries, industrial plants, vegetation, and forest fires.

3.20   _____ prevents the dissipation of pollutants by normal air currents.

3.21   High levels of ozone in the atmosphere can cause _____ smog, which can trigger respiratory problems.

3.22 _____ production has been theoretically linked to an increase in the occurrence of skin cancers caused by "holes" in the ozone layer.

3.23 CFCs are essential to modern uses of _____ and air conditioning.

3.24 _____ can cause damage in the form of atmospheric gas, dry particles, and acid.

3.25 Sulfur dioxide is a main component of _____ smog.

3.26 Sources of sulfur dioxide include engine exhaust, industry, domestic heating, and _____ eruptions.

ACTIVITY

God our Father vs. "Mother Earth"

Teaching on the environment is permeated with spiritual messages. We are told by environmental activists and writers that we must "save the earth" because she is our Mother. She is the one that gave us life. As her children, we are bound to heal her, preserve her, and worship her.

Earth worship is not new. Pagan religions throughout history have personified nature as a woman that is the "source and guiding force of creation." The ancient Babylonians worshiped the Goddess Ishtar, "Queen of Heaven." In Greek mythology, Gaea was the wife of Father Heaven and the giver of life to early man. The Native Americans sought harmony with a maternal spirit that was in every living thing. All of these goddesses were personifications of Mother Earth.

In this activity, you will examine the concept of "Mother Earth" in light of Scripture. Answer the questions below. **NOTE**: Be sure to support your answer with an explanation of at least two Bible verses/passages.

1. Genesis 3:19 states "…for out of [the earth] was thou taken; for dust thou art, and unto dust shalt thou return." In the context of the rest of Scripture, is the earth the creator of life, as the Mother Earth worshippers believe?

_____

_____

_____

2. Is "Mother Earth" the guiding force of creation? _____

_____

_____

_____

3. Is mankind bound to care for the earth because it is our "Mother"? _____

_____

_____

_____

4. Should mankind worship the Earth? _____

_____

_____

_____

✓ **Adult Check** _____

                                            Initial   **Date**

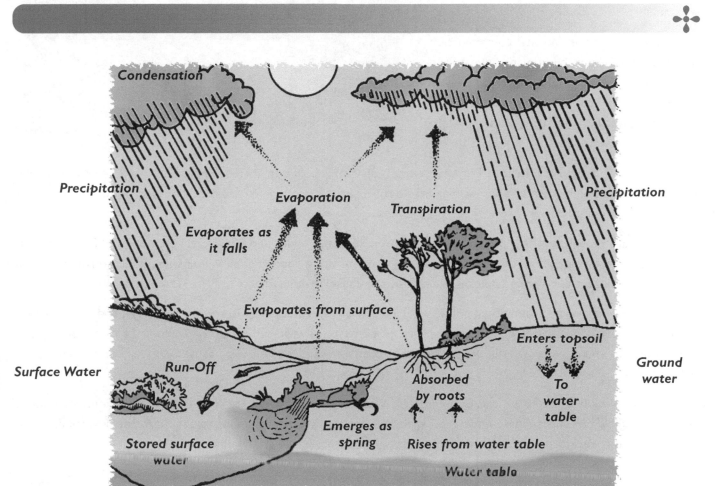

The Hydrological Cycle

Water Essentials

All of life is dependent upon water. It is supplied in three forms: gas, liquid, and solid. It appears as a gas in the form of clouds, fog, and water vapor. As a liquid, it manifests as rain, oceans, lakes, and underground springs. Water takes the form of a solid in snow, ice, and hail.

In its three forms, water is distributed throughout the earth in what is known as the **hydrological cycle**. The hydrological cycle is the continuous movement of water between the earth's surface and the atmosphere. Water in the form of vapor leaves the surface of living and nonliving things and enters the atmosphere. The vapor is collected in the atmosphere in the form of a cloud. The vapor is then formed into rain or snow, known as precipitation, which falls to the Earth's surface. It is either absorbed into the soil, falls into a body of water, or runs into a river or stream.

The water that is absorbed into the soil is used by plants to grow. Any excess water in the soil filters down into underground reservoirs. The cycle begins all over again when water is evaporated from the surface of leaves, skin, rivers, oceans, and soil.

Water Pollution. Billions of gallons of water are contaminated every day by the activities of both man and nature. Millions of tons of toxic chemicals are spewed forth every day from volcanoes and distributed over oceans and lakes. Refineries and factories throughout the world dump tons of solid and liquid wastes into coastal waters, rivers, and streams.

Because water is life, its contamination will affect the lives of the humans, animals, and plants that use it. Depending upon the degree and the source of contamination, it can lead to sickness, death, or even the extinction of a species in an affected area.

© Eric Wunrow

Sources of Water Pollution. Primary sources of water pollution include industrial waste, agriculture, and sewage. Industry pollutes water sources mainly by pouring waste into rivers, streams, or oceans. Some factories have been known to dump wastes into city sewage systems.

Agriculture can cause water pollution with the overuse of pesticides and fertilizers. Pesticides and fertilizers that are used in farming can seep down into the ground contaminating underground water sources. Although most pesticides and fertilizers decompose quickly, excess use can cause adverse effects.

Sewage is wastewater from either domestic or industrial sources. Domestic sewage is the by-product of bathing, bodily waste, cooking, etc. If not properly disposed of, domestic sewage can cause the spread of harmful bacteria. In many countries and regions without water treatment plants, sewage is the leading cause of water contamination and consequently, disease.

Water pollution can also be caused indirectly by solid waste disposal and forms of air pollution. Solid waste buried in landfills can contaminate underground water supplies by allowing toxins to seep into the surrounding soil. Chemicals and toxins dispersed by vehicle and industrial exhaust in the atmosphere can pollute precipitation, which can then pollute ground water supplies.

Types of Water Pollutants. Water pollutants are either chemical, organic, or physical materials. Physical materials are the most noticeable type of water pollution. You can see the effects of sediments or trash in water. Soil erosion around rivers, lakes, or streams can cause sediments to accumulate in large amounts, making the water appear cloudy. Water that is contaminated with sediments can hinder plant growth. It can also disrupt the reproductive cycles of some fish.

Solid waste that is dumped into water sources can pollute shorelines and waterways, making them hazardous to humans and animals. Discarded glass bottles, plastic and styrofoam containers, aluminum cans, paper products, etc., can contaminate the environment by adding toxins directly into water sources. Broken glass and rusted cans in rivers, streams, or lakes can present recreational dangers to humans. Plastic products, such as plastic bags, are often eaten by birds, fish, or other animals. The plastic, which cannot be digested, usually leads to the animal's death.

Organic pollutants include disease-causing organisms and overabundant organic matter. Water supplies that are contaminated with disease-causing organisms cause the deaths of over 10 million people each year worldwide. A majority of the people are from undeveloped countries with little or no water treatment system. Even in countries that have elaborate systems of water purification, such as the U. S., thousands of people get sick every year from drinking contaminated water.

An overabundance of organic matter in water supplies can lead to a process known as **eutrophication**. Eutrophication begins when fertilizers and other agricultural chemicals that are washed into water supplies cause certain aquatic plants, such as algae, to grow at accelerated rates. The algae's death then leads to **putrefaction**. Putrefaction is the decomposition of organic matter by microorganisms. In addition to their consumption of decaying matter, the microorganisms consume great amounts of dissolved oxygen. The depletion of oxygen can lead to the death of fish and plant life.

Chemical pollutants include pesticides, petroleum products, lead, mercury, and other toxins. Pesticides enter the water cycle through agricultural or domestic use. Pesticides that do not decay naturally present the worst threat to human and animal life. If used in excess of recommended amounts, they can become toxic.

Pollution caused by petroleum products is probably the most notorious form of water contamination. Oil spills are usually caused by an accident involving a tanker or an oil rig, and thankfully, are not an everyday occurrence. Nevertheless, oil spills can cause great harm to the plant and animal life in the affected shoreline area.

Another form of petroleum dumping that is equally damaging to the environment because of its more widespread occurrence is the improper disposal of engine oil. Oil or other chemicals that are dumped onto the ground can seep down into underground water supplies, causing contamination.

©Eric Wunrow

Water supplies with harmful levels of metals such as lead, mercury, and copper can cause adverse health effects, especially to children and the elderly. Lead, mercury, and copper occur naturally in the soil. However, aging water systems made with these metals can increase their quantities in water supplies. Wells are particularly susceptible to metal contamination.

✤ **Matching.**

3.27 _____ the continuous movement of water between the Earth's surface and the atmosphere

3.28 _____ pollutes water sources by dumping wastes in rivers, streams, and oceans

3.29 _____ the leading cause of water contamination in countries without water treatment plants

3.30 _____ a source of water pollution caused by the overuse of pesticides and fertilizers

3.31 _____ caused by an overabundance of organic matter in water supplies

3.32 _____ the decomposition of organic matter by microorganisms

3.33 _____ a chemical pollutant that can enter the water cycle through agricultural or domestic use

3.34 _____ can cause the contamination of underground water supplies if poured on the ground

3.35 _____ a metal that leaks into water supplies via the soil or aging water systems

a. agriculture

b. eutrophication

c. hydrological cycle

d. industry

e. lead

f. pesticides

g. petroleum

h. putrefaction

i. sewage

Soil Essentials

Equally important to the survival of life is soil. Soil is the top layer of the earth's crust. It consists of inorganic materials, organic materials, water, and other nutrients. Inorganic materials consist of rocks, stones, pebbles, sand, etc. The inorganic composition of a particular plot of land is determined by the underlying layer of rock and the effects of weather. Inorganic materials can range in size from large rocks to microscopic particles.

The organic materials consist of living and dead debris from plants and animals. Partially decayed organic matter is known as humus. Humus fosters the productive growth of crops such as corn, beans, and potatoes. Both organic and inorganic materials in the soil help to purify water as it passes through the hydrological cycle.

Water and other elements foster the growth of plants and other organisms living in the soil. Water is necessary for the absorption of elements that are essential to plant growth. The amount of water in the soil contributes to its physical nature and viability.

The daily activities of man, animals, and plants produces waste that can contaminate the soil. Body elimination, decay, and respiration create substances that are then added to the environment. As long as life exists on earth, the production of waste cannot be avoided. It can be controlled, however.

Soil pollution generally refers to the buildup of waste, both organic and inorganic, that can adversely affect human, animal, and plant life. Organic wastes are by-products of living matter. For example, dried leaves are a form of organic waste. Organic waste is biodegradable—it can be broken down by other organisms into a reusable form.

Returning to the previous example, when a leaf falls from a tree, it immediately begins the process of decay. Water, soil, and microorganisms decompose the leaf. The organic matter that the leaf once consisted of is then broken down into various chemical substances that can provide nutrition for other living organisms. Organic waste is an important part of a healthy environment.

Many man-made products are nondegradable. If discarded, they become inorganic wastes that cannot be broken down by the environment within a short period. Plastic, rubber, glass, and styrofoam are some examples of man-made products that do not decompose for a long time. Their chemical make-up gives them the ability to be exposed to decaying influences with little or no effect. This attribute is a plus for modern life but a minus for waste disposal. Most nondegradable products can remain buried for years without any decomposition.

Man-made wastes that are nondegradable and may threaten the health of those that are exposed to them are known as hazardous wastes. Hazardous wastes are solid, liquid, or gas wastes that are toxic, flammable, corrosive, reactive, or radioactive. Hazardous wastes are usually the chemical by-products of industrial, medical, agricultural, and domestic activity.

Improperly disposed of solid or hazardous wastes can affect the quality of the soil, preventing it from acting as a nutrient base for plants and a filtration system for water. Consequently, soils that are polluted can affect the quality of crops and underground water supplies, disrupting the health of humans and animals. Soils polluted with solid and hazardous wastes can also alter the air quality by emitting toxic fumes into the atmosphere.

Controlling Soil Pollution. In the United States, over 250 million metric tons of solid waste is produced every year. This breaks down to approximately 3 to 4 pounds of waste per citizen per day. Controlling the pollution of soil by solid and hazardous waste can be a daunting task. That is why many people believe that the first and foremost way to control pollution is to decrease its production.

What about the waste that *must* be produced? How can it be controlled in such a way as to lessen the effects of soil pollution on human, animal, and plant life?

In developed countries, sanitary landfills are the most common means of solid waste disposal. Landfill sites are carefully chosen and prepared to ensure the least amount of soil and water pollution. Waste is deposited into the fill in thin layers. Each layer of waste is then compacted by bulldozers and other equipment until it is approximately 10 feet thick. Then each layer is covered with a thin layer of soil. Landfills can require large plots of land and, if not properly ventilated, leak toxic fumes. However, many landfill sites are safe enough to be reclaimed for recreational purposes, such as parks, golf courses, and baseball fields.

Incinerators are another widely used form of waste management. Incinerators burn solid waste materials and trace gases. In addition to reducing the need for more landfills, incinerators also reduce the use of fossil fuels in the production of energy. Many incinerators are designed to produce electricity when refuse is burned. However, incinerators also eject pollutants into the air.

Composting disposes of solid biodegradable wastes through the implementation of the process of decomposition. Like landfills, layers of waste are piled on top of one another and then condensed. However, wastes are condensed through the natural process of decomposition brought about by moisture and heat acting on the waste materials. The substance that is produced is known as compost. Compost can be produced and sold as fertilizer.

In addition to proper methods of disposal, pollution can be reduced by recycling. Recycling is the process by which certain waste materials, such as plastic, glass, aluminum and paper, are prepared for reuse. Recycling reduces the demand for solid waste disposal. However, recycling is much more costly, and it creates other environmental concerns. As one writer has noted, "producing paperboard burger containers yields more air and water pollution and consumes more energy than does manufacturing polystyrene clamshells. It takes more water to recycle newsprint than to make it afresh." Chemicals used to recycle paper and plastics are sometimes more harmful to the environment than the chemicals and waste produced by new products.

Because of the potential dangers of hazardous waste, its control is of particular concern to human health. Hazardous wastes are nondegradable and, therefore, must be managed by means of treatment plants, storage sites, and recycling. Treatment plants may burn hazardous wastes, dilute them with water or other chemicals, or melt them down into a non-toxic substance.

Hazardous wastes are also dumped into storage containers. The containers are built of glass, clay, plastic, and steel. The containers help to keep the hazardous wastes from contaminating the surrounding soil.

A small portion of hazardous wastes can be recycled. Oils, household cleaners, and other solvents can be treated and then reused. Many gas stations and service centers collect engine oil for recycling.

Underline.

3.36   Soil pollution is caused by the buildup of (**organic and inorganic, solid and liquid, hazardous and biodegradable**) wastes that can adversely affect human, animal, and plant life.

3.37   (**Biodegradable, Nondegradable**) wastes can be broken down by other organisms into a reusable form.

3.38   Discarded plastic, rubber, glass, and styrofoam are examples of (**biodegradable, nondegradable**) wastes.

3.39   (**Solid, Hazardous, Domestic**) wastes are solid, liquid, or gas wastes that are toxic, flammable, corrosive, reactive, or radioactive.

3.40   Improperly disposed of solid or hazardous wastes can affect the (**accessibility, quality, abundance**) of water, soil, and air.

3.41   Waste is deposited into (**landfills, incinerators, compost piles**) in thin layers which are then compacted and covered with soil.

3.42   (**Landfills, Incinerators, Compost piles**) reduce the need for landfills by burning solid wastes.

3.43   (**Landfills, Incinerators, Compost piles**) dispose of solid biodegradable wastes through the implementation of the process of decomposition.

3.44   (**Composting, Recycling, Incineration**) is the process by which certain waste materials, such as plastic, glass, aluminum, and paper, are prepared for reuse.

3.45   (**Biodegradable, Organic, Hazardous**) wastes are managed with treatment plants, storage sites, and recycling.

A Balanced Approach

As the twenty-sixth President of the United States, Theodore Roosevelt made the preservation of the environment an important political and social concern. However, he was not an "environmentalist" in the modern sense of the term. He did not believe that nature should be preserved for nature's sake. As a Christian and an American, he believed that the nation's natural resources were to be managed for the benefit of future generations. "His love of nature did not obscure his comprehension of its fallen estate and its ultimate subservience to the interests of man," one author observed.

Theodore Roosevelt understood that it was man's responsibility to care for the environment as it had been Adam's responsibility to care for the Garden. Roosevelt's approach to stewardship is termed "conservationism." During his second term of office, President Roosevelt led the conservationist movement by setting aside millions of acres of timberland and establishing wildlife preserves and national parks. He also urged the American people in speeches and essays to think differently about their natural resources.

President Theodore Roosevelt

Boldly articulating his concerns for the future, he once said, "I recognize the right and duty of this generation to develop and use the natural resources of our land; but I do not recognize the right to waste them, or to rob, by wasteful use, the generations that come after us."

Central to Theodore Roosevelt's conservationist ideas was the protection of the American people. Roosevelt asserted that a person's health was directly related to his or her environment. Therefore, to preserve nature was to preserve mankind.

As Christians searching for a balanced approach to the environment, we can learn much from Theodore Roosevelt. Unlike many environmental activists today, he did not just want to "save the earth" or "save the whales." Ultimately, Roosevelt wanted to "save the humans." We should have similar aims.

❖ **Short answer.**

3.46   How was Theodore Roosevelt's approach to the environment different from modern-day environmentalists?

_____

_____

3.47   Why did Roosevelt set aside millions of acres for national parks and wildlife? _____

_____

_____

3.48   What was the motivating factor behind Roosevelt's conservationist ideas? _____

_____

_____

ACTIVITY

Conserving Your Environment

One of the amazing things about the creation is that it is so resilient. Since the Flood, both mankind and nature have spewed pollutants into the air at a rate of several billions tons per year. And yet, the earth's atmosphere has changed little. On a global scale, carbon dioxide, sulfur, nitrogen, and other pollutants do little to endanger the respiration of plants, animals, and humans. Clean air is not scarce.

So how is this possible, especially with all the changes that modern man has "forced" upon the environment. There are many reasons that the creation is so resilient. One is the growth of plants. In His benevolent wisdom, God made plants, animals, and people dependent upon one another. The life of one affects the other. Mankind not only relies on plants to feed themselves and their livestock, it needs plants to breathe. Plants produce the oxygen that mankind and animals depend on for life. In turn, mankind and animals exhale carbon dioxide, which plants need to live. Plant growth is God's way of reducing air pollution.

In many urban areas, air quality has been greatly affected by the reduction of plant growth and the increase of vehicle emissions and industrial activity. Growing more trees and plants in these areas can significantly reduce air pollutants. As one scientist has noted, some species of plants, such as Alder and English ivy, consume carbon monoxide as well as carbon dioxide. Many plants can absorb other toxins, such as sulfur and nitrogen. Particulates can also be removed from the air by plants.

In this activity, you will conserve your environment by growing a tree or another type of plant. If you cannot plant a tree outside, growing a small plant in a home is also beneficial. The air quality in your home can be affected by burning wood or fossil fuels for heating and cooking purposes.

Step 1: Decide what kind of plant you would like to grow. Depending upon where you grow the plant, discuss with a parent or a teacher what type of plant would be best suited for the environment that you have to grow it in. You might need to visit a plant nursery to help you to make your decision. Some trees or plants need more water or light. Others need a certain kind of soil. Make an informed decision. The life of your plant will depend upon it.

Step 2: Buy the seeds and other supplies. If you decide to plant a tree, you might want to buy or obtain a shoot. A shoot is a new tree that has begun to grow. Seeds, shoots, and other supplies, such as potting soil and fertilizer, can be purchased at a plant nursery or at some hardware stores. Talk to a sales representative to get the supplies you need.

Step 3: Plant your seeds or tree shoot. According to the directions on the seed package or given to you by the nursery attendant, place your seeds or shoot in the soil. Be sure your plant is buried at the right depth and in a place that will ensure the growth of your plant. Seeds or shoots that are planted improperly, will not grow. If you are growing a plant indoors, place it in a container that will help its growth. Make sure the container allows for proper drainage and root growth. Soil, whether in a container or outdoors, should contain the right amount nutrients needed for growth. Some plants need acidic soil to survive, others do not.

Step 4: Tend and care for your plant. Depending on the plant, it will need a certain amount of water and nutrients to grow. Most new growth, such as seeds, needs moist soil to sprout. Some plants also need extra food to grow. Continue to follow the directions on the seed package or consult with a plant nursery worker to make sure that you are caring for your plant correctly. You can also read a book on gardening to find out more information.

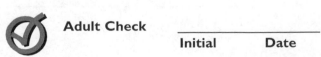

Adult Check _____

Initial   **Date**

Review the material in this section in preparation for the Self Test. The Self Test will check your mastery of this particular section as well as your knowledge of the previous sections.

SELF TEST 3

Answer the following *true* **or** *false* (each answer, 2 points).

3.01 _____ Your environment consists of all the living and nonliving things that surround and support you.

3.02 _____ The catastrophic events surrounding the Flood drastically changed the environment.

3.03 _____ After the Flood, the high humidity produced a "greenhouse effect" over the entire earth.

3.04 _____ God split mankind into nations so that it would "fill the earth and subdue it."

3.05 _____ God intended mankind to be subservient to the environment.

3.06 _____ The cultural mandate to "subdue" the environment allows mankind to use natural resources without regard for future generations.

3.07 _____ The best means to avoid being infected by an STD is to abstain from eating in restaurants that do not conform to a high standard of cleanliness.

3.08 _____ Proper waste disposal and clean water are the primary means of promoting public health.

3.09 _____ Psychological dependence is marked by a state of mental and physical abnormality when the drug is withdrawn.

3.010 _____ Drug abuse is the taking of any drug in a manner that can help bolster your physical or psychological state.

Underline the correct answer (each answer, 2 points).

3.011 The (**atmosphere, exosphere, mesosphere**) consists of a mixture of gases and particles including oxygen, nitrogen, hydrogen, carbon dioxide, water vapor, and dust.

3.012 The ozone layer is part of the (**troposphere, exosphere, stratosphere**).

3.013 Air pollution can lead to (**digestive, respiratory, industrial**) problems.

3.014 The air is polluted by (**natural and human, domestic and industrial, organic and aquatic**) sources.

3.015 (**Biodegradable, Nondegradable**) wastes can be broken down by other organisms into a reusable form.

3.016 (**Solid, Hazardous, Domestic**) wastes are solid, liquid, or gas wastes that are toxic, flammable, corrosive, reactive, or radioactive.

3.017 Improperly disposed of solid or hazardous wastes can affect the (**accessibility, quality, abundance**) of water, soil, and air.

3.018 Waste is deposited into (**landfills, incinerators, compost piles**) in thin layers which are then compacted and covered with soil.

3.019 (**Landfills, Incinerators, Compost piles**) reduce the need for landfills by burning solid wastes.

3.020   (**Landfills, Incinerators, Compost piles**) dispose of solid biodegradable wastes through the implementation of the process of decomposition.

3.021   (**Composting, Recycling, Incineration**) is the process by which certain waste materials, such as plastic, glass, aluminum, and paper are prepared for reuse.

3.022   Tobacco leaves and stems contain an addictive drug known as (**carbon monoxide, tar, nicotine**).

3.023   (**Smokers, nonsmokers**) more frequently develop chronic bronchitis, lung cancer, heart disease, and emphysema than (**smokers, nonsmokers**).

3.024   The only cure for the common cold and the flu is (**cold medication, rest, a ventilator**).

3.025   Both Type I and Type II diabetics can help keep their insulin levels near normal by following a strict diet that is low in (**protein, carbohydrates, fat**).

animal	*fossil fuels*	*steroid*	*photochemical*	*VOCs*
CFC	*hygiene*	*nuclear*	*thermal inversion*	*vectors*
drug	*industrial*	*ozone*	*trees*	*volcanic*

Complete the following sentences, using the words above (each problem, 1 point).

3.026   In the last 100 years, the burning of _____ by man has significantly increased the level of CO_2 in the atmosphere.

3.027   Carbon dioxide is a natural product of _____ and human life.

3.028   Levels of CO_2 in the atmosphere can be reduced by increasing the use of _____ power and by planting _____ in urban areas.

3.029   _____ is formed in the atmosphere when chemicals, called volatile organic compounds (VOCs), and nitrogen dioxide (NO_2) are acted upon by sunlight.

3.030   _____ are emitted into the atmosphere by gas-powered vehicles, chemical refineries, industrial plants, vegetation, and forest fires.

3.031   _____ prevents the dissipation of pollutants by normal air currents.

3.032   High levels of ozone in the atmosphere can cause _____ smog, which can trigger respiratory problems.

3.033   _____ production has been theoretically linked to an increase in the occurrence of skin cancers caused by "holes" in the ozone layer.

3.034   Sulfur dioxide is a main component of _____ smog.

3.035   Sources of sulfur dioxide include engine exhaust, industry, domestic heating, and _____ eruptions.

3.036   A _____ is a chemical substance used to treat, prevent, or diagnose a disease or alter on or more functions of the body.

3.037   A _____ has side effects of extreme rage, paranoia, and stunted growth.

3.038   The contraction of infectious diseases can be avoided by practicing good _____ , avoiding contact with _____ , and boosting your immune system with immunizations.

Match the following items (each answer, 1 point).

3.039	_____	the continuous movement of water between the Earth's surface and the atmosphere
3.040	_____	pollutes water sources by dumping wastes in rivers, streams, and oceans
3.041	_____	the leading cause of water contamination in countries without water treatment plants
3.042	_____	a source of water pollution caused by the overuse of pesticides and fertilizers
3.043	_____	caused by an overabundance of organic matter in water supplies
3.044	_____	the decomposition of organic matter by microorganisms
3.045	_____	a chemical pollutant that can enter the water cycle through agricultural or domestic use
3.046	_____	can cause the contamination of underground water supplies if poured on the ground
3.047	_____	a metal that leaks into water supplies via the soil or aging water systems
3.048	_____	depends upon the production of disease specific antibodies to destroy harmful bacteria
3.049	_____	increases the activity of the central nervous system
3.050	_____	reduces the activity of the central nervous system
3.051	_____	caused by the reproduction of a small infectious agent, which produces poisons that destroy cells

a. agriculture

b. bacterial infection

c. depressants

d. eutrophication

e. humoral immunity

f. hydrological cycle

g. industry

h. lead

i. pesticides

j. petroleum

k. putrefaction

l. sewage

m. stimulants

Answer the following questions (each answer, 5 points).

3.052   How was Theodore Roosevelt's approach to the environment different from modern-day environmentalists?

_____

_____

_____

3.053   Why did Roosevelt set aside millions of acres for national parks and wildlife? _____

_____

_____

3.054   What was the motivating factor behind Roosevelt's conservationist ideas? _____

_____

_____

Multiple choice (each answer, 3 points).

3.055   When will Christians no longer be troubled by disease or death? _____
        a. When they are in Heaven.
        b. When they decide not to sin.
        c. When they stop exposing themselves to infectious agents.
        d. When everyone in the world is vaccinated.

3.056   Why is drunkenness considered a sin? _____
        a. It indicates a desire to find peace and fulfillment in the things of the world rather than in God.
        b. It is pleasurable.
        c. It can cause you to do and say foolish things.
        d. It can lead to alcoholism.

3.057   What disease is characterized by the unrestrained growth of abnormal cells on or in the tissues of the body?
_____
        a. protozoan infection
        b. cancer
        c. diabetes
        d. coronary heart disease

80
/100

Alpha Omega Publications®

804 N. 2nd Ave. E.
Rock Rapids, IA 51246-1759
800-622-3070
www.aop.com

EL9705 – Sep '17

ISBN 978-0-7403-0

W7-DGL-121

9 780740 301